PARENT-TEACHER COLLECTION

CLASSIC
to
CONTEMPORARY

Famous Artists and Activities

PARENT-TEACHER COLLECTION

By
Harriet Kinghorn
and
Lisa Lewis-Spicer

D1473795

Cover Illustration by
Margo De Paulis

Inside Illustrations by
Darcy Myers

Icons designed by
Steve Volavka

Publishers
T.S. Denison & Company, Inc.
Minneapolis, Minnesota

T.S. DENISON & CO., INC.

Acknowledgments

We want to thank Nancy L. Reed, Bianca I. Katz, and Connie Selle for their help in the preparation of the manuscript.

Standard Book Number: 513-02170-1
Classic to Contemporary Famous Artists and Activities
Copyright © 1993 by the T.S. Denison & Co., Inc.
9601 Newton Avenue South
Minneapolis, Minnesota 55431

Printed in the USA

INTRODUCTION

There are many reasons for studying and creating art. Through study, we can learn about the important achievements and talents of famous artists and their work and we can try to understand what they hoped to communicate to the world. By participating in art activities that are related to these artists' styles, we can practice the skills of observing, analyzing, and creating. We can attempt to put ourselves into their minds, hearts, hands, and eyes. Once we do this, we inevitably learn more about ourselves, as well as the artists we study.

In writing this book, our hope was to bring the beauty and knowledge of artists and their art to you, the curious child, the student, the teacher, and the parent. Use the following biographies, activities, evaluations, bibliography, glossary, and extension activities to enrich your understanding of artists and their art. You may also find this book helpful in enriching your own artwork and yourself as an artist.

We believe importance of encouraging livelong learning opportunities that promote organizational skills, and better enable us to communicate, make comparisons, and solve problems. These lifelong learning skills, in turn, support the learner's self-expression and self-esteem through creative thinking.

We hope that *Classic to Contemporary* will provide you with many hours of creative thinking and learning. Above all, we hope the reading and activities in this book make you more aware and appreciative, not only of the featured artists, but of the blossoming young artists around you.

> Harriet Kinghorn
> Lisa Lewis-Spicer

TABLE OF CONTENTS

TABLE OF CONTENTS

SUGGESTIONS FOR PARENTS AND TEACHERS

1. Read the included biography to obtain background information on the specific artist. (For school use, the biographies may be reproduced on both sides of a sheet of paper, or the two sheets can be stapled along with the corresponding activity sheet to make a booklet on each artist.) You may wish to read other articles and books on this particular artist and you may wish to consult the bibliography for pertinent titles regarding the artist of your choosing.

2. After reading some background information on the specific artist, do the corresponding project suggested on the activity sheet. Although we have made a specific project that relates to each artist, you or a child may have a different project to create that correlatives with the artist. If you should decide to create a project other than the one indicated on the enclosed activity sheet, the evaluation questions/statements will coincide nicely with it. Since a child has the choice of writing on four out of the six questions/statements, the child does not need to respond to one that doesn't relate to his/her projects. The child need only respond to questions/statements which pertain to his/her creative project.

3. When the child/children have responded to the questions and statements on the evaluation sheet, you may want to share and discuss those responses with each other. Appreciate the variety of responses you will hear.

4. Remember art has many purposes besides being beautiful. Art can be the result of a personal expression, an emotional release, and/or a learning experience.

BACKGROUND INFORMATION

ARTIST: _____ NAME: _____

ABOUT AN ARTIST

Find and read at least two sources about the artist that you are studying at this time. The sources might be an encyclopedia, book, filmstrip, newspaper, magazine, or another reference book.

Title of Media	Where it was obtained

OTHER INFORMATION DISCOVERED ABOUT THE ARTIST

_____
_____
_____
_____
_____
_____
_____
_____
_____
_____
_____
_____
_____

Use the back of this sheet if you need more space.

Rosa Bonheur
(bo NUR)
1822–1899

One of France's most successful and celebrated painters in the 1800s was a strong and independent-minded woman in a time when men dominated most professions. This painter, highly esteemed for her accurate anatomical drawings of animals, was Rosa Bonheur.

Rosa Bonheur was born in Bordeaux, France, in 1822. Her full name was Marie Rosalie Bonheur. Her father, a landscape painter and drawing teacher, instructed Rosa, as well and her three younger siblings, in drawing and painting. The four Bonheur children all became artists specializing in animal subjects. When Rosa was a young teenager, she often visited the Louvre Museum in Paris (where she and her family lived) to study the works of the great masters. In order to strengthen her skills, Rosa copied the paintings of several famous artists. By the time she was seventeen she was selling her work and helping to support her family.

Throughout her childhood Rosa was fascinated with animals. At the age of ten she rejected an apprenticeship to a dressmaker, preferring instead to go to the forest, the Bois de Bologne, and sketch the animals she found there. Determined to accurately portray the animals she painted, Rosa studied each animal's anatomy with great patience and diligence. She often dissected animal parts she obtained from butchers and also visited slaughterhouses to study in detail the subjects which she captured so convincingly on canvas. So that she would not be scorned and ridiculed while she studied the anatomy of her animal subjects at slaughterhouses, horse fairs, and cattle markets, Rosa dressed in men's clothing. During the mid-1800s it was practically unheard of for a woman to visit these places, thus, Rosa wore men's clothing and cut her hair short so that she could work without interruption. Rosa remained an unconventional and fiercely independent woman throughout her lifetime. Although she never married, Rosa formed a long lasting relationship with a fellow artist, Natalie Micas. Rosa was also inspired, by the literature of George Sand, another prominent woman of the nineteenth century who wore men's clothing and who took a man's name as her own.

Rosa Bonheur's paintings were celebrated for their bold technique, their striking color compositions, and their subjects' lively energized movements across the canvas. Rosa was very interested in drawing directly from nature and the realistic effects of light in her work illustrate her careful observations of natural light and space. Her work *Red Oxen of Cantal*, a piece resulting from her studies of rural scenes of the French countryside, won Rosa a gold medal in 1848. In June of 1865, the Empress Eugénie presented Rosa Bonheur with the cross of the French Legion of Honor. Rosa was the first woman artist ever to receive this high honor.

Rosa Bonheur received much acclaim and attention during her lifetime. She exhibited regularly at the annual Paris Salon until her retirement in 1853. After her retirement she moved to her chateau on the outskirts of the Forest of Fontainebleau. Not only did Rosa experience success in France, but she was also admired in Belgium, Portugal, Spain, Mexico, England and America.

Perhaps Bonheur's most famous work, first exhibited in 1853, is her large painting entitled *The Horses Fair*. *The Horse Fair*, now hanging in the Metropolitan Museum in New York City, is a dramatically bold piece depicting a group of spirited horses dominating and surrounding the men who are trying to control them. The interplay of dark and light, the depth of the colors, and the movement of the realistically portrayed subjects all combine to present a stunning piece of work.

Rosa Bonheur was one of the most successful of female painters in the 1800s. She diligently prepared for her life's work, conveying on canvas not only the energized and independent spirit of her subjects, but her own true spirit as well.

Name: _____

ROSA BONHEUR

VOCABULARY: texture, simulate, realistic, anatomy

MATERIALS: paper and pencil; paints, crayons or markers, and materials for textures.

ACTIVITIES:

1.   Look closely at some of Rosa Bonheur's animal paintings. Observe the texture of her animals. Do you think the animals look realistic?

2.   Practice making various kinds of textures on a sheet of paper to simulate animal fur, hair, feathers, and wool.

3.   Make a picture that includes at least one animal in it. Use texture to make the animal look realistic and interesting. Remember, Rosa Bonheur spent many years learning to draw her animals just like she wanted them. Like Rosa, keep practicing!

Name: _____

THINKING ABOUT ROSA BONHEUR AND ME

Respond to four or more of the following questions/statements.

1. How do you think you would feel if you wanted to go to an art school but you were not permitted to attend because you were a girl?

2. Since girls were not permitted to go to art schools during Rosa Bonheur's time, she went to the Louvre (LOO-vr) to observe and copy art. What and where is the Louvre?

3. List twelve or more words that relate to Rosa Bonheur or her work.

4. Many artists, including Rosa Bonheur, have had their paintings judged in contests. If you were a judge for a painting contest, what specific things would you look for in each piece of art?

5. Write the title of your favorite art piece by Rosa Bonheur. Why is it your favorite?

6. Write one or more paragraphs about what you have learned about this artist and/or what you have learned through your own creative project relating to this artist. Write this information on the opposite side of this sheet or on a separate sheet of paper.

Margaret Bourke-White

1904–1971

One of America's most outstanding pioneers in the world of photography was Margaret Bourke-White. Not only a brilliant photographer, but an outstanding lecturer and writer as well. Her commitment to her work and the strength of her vision gave us the photo-essay, Bourke-White's contribution to photojournalism. The photo-essay is a carefully planned and often powerful sequence of photographs and captions. In addition to taking the pictures, the photographer usually writes the captions that accompany the pictures. The photo-essay as we know it today, was refined by Margaret Bourke-White and is the mainstay of news and picture magazines. In addition to producing a variety of photographs on factories, machinery, industrial workers, and on the horrors of war, Margaret Bourke-White produced photographic essays on world-famous leaders such as Mahatma Gandhi, Winston Churchill, Madame Chiang Kai-Shek, and Pope Pius XII.

Margaret Bourke-White was born in New York City, on June 14, 1904, the youngest of three children. Her mother, Minnie Bourke, and her father, Joseph White, (who was an engineer and inventor) encouraged her curiosity and fascination with everything from machinery to snakes. Young Margaret was very interested in animal life and she particularly loved studying snakes. She wanted to become a herpetologist — a person who studies reptiles and amphibians. After studying at Columbia University, where she took a photography course with Clarence White, the University of Michigan, and Western Reserve University in Cleveland, she finally graduated from Cornell University in Ithaca, New York, where she studied biology and philosophy.

In order to earn money while she was studying at Cornell the idea occurred to her to take photographs of the spectacularly scenic campus. She put her prints of the campus on sale and most of them sold. Then the *Cornell Alumni News* offered to pay her five dollars for a monthly picture of a campus building. Margaret received great praise from several architects who said she had a remarkable talent for photographing buildings. Margaret was excited with her success and she seriously considered pursuing photography as a profession even though she had a job offer to be assistant curator of herpetology at New York's Museum of Natural History. In 1927 Bourke-White began working in Cleveland — as a photographer.

As a photographer Bourke-White achieved immediate success. One of her first photographs was printed in *Architecture* magazine. Architects felt there was no one more capable of photographing a building than Margaret Bourke-White. She worked as a commercial photographer for bankers and industrialists as well as architects. In 1929 Henry R. Luce, the publisher of *Time* magazine, hired Margaret as a photographer for the new magazine, *Fortune* . At *Fortune* Margaret specialized in photographing factories, machinery, and industrial workers. A year later she was sent to Germany on assignment to record the industrialization of the country. Upon leaving Germany she traveled to the Soviet Union to take pictures of the Soviet's Five Year Plan — recording the industrialization plan initiated by the Bolshevik government.

Margaret Bourke-White was an avid adventurer and explorer, and traveled all over the world while on assignment for *Fortune* and *Life* magazines. In 1936 she became one of *Life's* first staff photographers. It was during her work for *Life* that she originated the concept of photojournalism and refined the use of photo-essays. The cover on *Life* magazine's first issue on November 11, 1936, featured Margaret's photograph of the huge concrete forms of Fort Peck Dam in Montana. In a nine-page story accompanying the photographs of the Montana construction project, Margaret intimately depicted the lives of the construction workers involved with the project. It was this kind of strong and sensitive portrayal that secured Bourke-White's outstanding reputation as a photojournalist.

Margaret Bourke-White became the first woman war correspondent when her assignments brought her to combat fields and concentration camps during World War II. Her pictures of the starving prisoners in the Nazi concentration camps, shocked the world into awareness. Sensitive to the plight of those much less fortunate, Margaret fought for freedom, justice, equality, and an end to human suffering. She frequently confronted danger, and while she may have been afraid, she never stopped taking pictures. She was the only American photographer in the Soviet Union when the Nazis bombed Moscow by the light of parachuted magnesium flares. She was also the first woman photographer in World War II assigned to the United States Armed Forces — while her ship was being torpedoed at night she continued to shoot pictures.

Margaret Bourke-White was a daring and brilliant pioneer of photography, capturing in pictures some of the most important moments in the twentieth century. In addition to her photographs she published several books of her war experiences including *Dear Fatherland, Rest Quietly* (1946), *Shooting the Russian War* (1943), *Purple Heart Valley* (1944), and *Halfway to Freedom* (1949). With the American novelist Erskine Caldwell, she published *You Have Seen Their Faces* (1934), *North of the Danube* (1939), and *Say, Is This the USA?* (1941).

On August 27, 1971, Margaret Bourke-White, a master photographer and a dynamic photojournalist, died from complications of Parkinson's Disease.

Name: _____

MARGARET BOURKE-WHITE

VOCABULARY: professional photographer, war correspondent, industrial photographer, World War II

MATERIALS: a large sheet of construction paper to represent a photo album cover, paper for pages in the album, unlined index cards for photos, black crayons or pencils, and glue.

ACTIVITIES:

1. Study Margaret Bourke-White's work as a professional photographer, a war correspondent, and an industrial photographer. Read and discuss as much about Margaret Bourke-White as possible so you will have many ideas for making imaginary photos of her work to put in a photo album.

2. Draw pictures on index cards that represent the black and white photos that Margaret Bourke-White took as a professional photographer. Glue your "photos" onto paper and design and decorate a construction paper cover for a booklet to represent a photo album that Bourke-White might have made of her work. Write an appropriate caption below each photo.

Name: _____

THINKING ABOUT MARGARET BOURKE-WHITE AND ME

Respond to four or more of the following questions/statements.

1. Describe what you think Maragret Bourke-White may have been like as a person.

2. If you were a professional photographer, what would you like to photograph?

3. If your were a photographer for a magazine publisher, which magazine would you like to work for and why?

4. What did you enjoy most and/or least about making a photo album of Margaret Bourke-White's photography.

5. What do you think were the three most interesting events that Margaret Bourke-White photographed?

6. Write one or more paragraphs about what you have learned about this artist and/or what you have learned through your own creative project relating to this artist. Write this information on the opposite side of this sheet or on a separate sheet of paper.

Leonardo da Vinci
(da VIN chee)
1452–1519

Painter. Sculptor. Inventor. Philosopher. Writer. Musician. Architect. Engineer. Mathematician. Leonardo da Vinci was all of these and much more. As one of the most versatile geniuses in history, Leonardo da Vinci's keen observation and knowledge about a vast array of subjects including anatomy, astronomy, botany, and biology made him a true Renaissance man. Today and during his lifetime, Leonardo is recognized as one of the most important representatives of Renaissance culture.

The Renaissance was a period of European history from about 1400 to approximately 1600 and it marked the end of the Middle Ages, sometimes known as 'medieval' times. The Renaissance was a period of great achievement in art, literature, and learning. The great sculptor, painter, and draftsman Michelangelo was productive at this time, as were the writers Cervantes and Shakespeare, and the explorer, Christopher Columbus, who searched for a new route to the Indies.

Leonardo was an excellent observer and a meticulous notetaker. He recorded his thoughts and ideas about art, engineering, and science in many notebooks, some of which have been preserved. He wrote notes backwards so that one would have to hold them up to a mirror in order to read them. Many of Leonardo's ideas were far ahead of their time. His notebooks contained sketches of flying machines and parachutes, designs for cathedrals and bridges, and investigations concerning the circulation of blood in the human body, and theories about the Earth's movement around the sun. Although few of his ideas were ever carried out, some of Leonardo da Vinci's paintings and drawings from his notebooks still survive. They are some of the greatest masterpieces in the art world.

Leonardo was born in the mountain village of Vinci, Italy, west of Florence, on April 15, 1492. His father, Ser Piero da Vinci (da means "from" in Italian), was an ambitious and successful lawyer. He did not marry Leonardo's mother, Caterina, a young peasant woman, because she was poor and had no dowry (money) to bring to the marriage. Leonardo probably lived with his mother for the first four or five years of his life, but later he lived with his grandfather, father, and new stepmother in his grandfather's house in Vinci.

At the age of fifteen, Leonardo traveled to Florence to become an assistant to the very talented and respected painter and sculptor, Andrea del Verrochio. Together, Verrochio and Leonardo worked on the painting *The Baptism of Christ*. Leonardo painted the kneeling angel in the left corner and the landscape in the background. When people in Florence saw the painting, they thought Leonardo's angle was the most beautiful and realistic part of the picture. Verrochio and his many apprentices realized a masterful painter was emerging. They detected Leonardo's unique style in which his painted figures looked as if they were breathing, moving, and actually alive. His outlines were slightly blurred, not bluntly defined, and his figures were graceful, calm, and serene looking. An overall aura of mystery, as well as mastery, in his paintings illustrates Leonardo's skilled placement of dark and light colors. Leonardo was the first painter to use the pyramid concept of design in his work. Some of Leonardo's works in which you can see the composition of this pyramid design are *The Lady with the Ermine* in the National Museum in Cracow, Poland, and *The Virgin and Child with Saint Anne* in the Louvre Museum in Paris, France. Leonardo's artistic principles concerning the pyramid design greatly influenced the Italian Renaissance painters Michelangelo (1475–1564) and Raphael (1483–1520). Leonardo was also one of the first artists to portray the mother of Jesus smiling and playing with her baby. In the painting *La Madonna Benois* in the Hermitage Museum in Leningrad, Russia, we see Mary, the mother of Jesus, smiling and holding her baby as he curiously inspects a sprig of flowers she is holding.

Leonardo da Vinci is perhaps most famous for a portrait currently hanging in the Louvre Museum in Paris. *The Mona Lisa*, also called *La Gioconda*, was painted in 1503 and is undoubtedly the most famous portrait in the world. Although originally much larger, the *Mona Lisa* now measures 30 1/4" x 20 7/8." Experts believe that the sides of the *Mona Lisa* were trimmed, so that the painting could fit into a particular frame. The painting depicts a lady, sitting with her hands gently folded one over the other, set against a distant Alpine landscape. Part of the painting's great allure is that no one is quite sure who the original sitter was. Viewers of the *Mona Lisa* are captivated by her mysterious and unforgettable smile, and her gaze, which seems to follow you wherever you stand. Like many of Leonardo's previous paintings, the figure of the *Mona Lisa* forms a pyramid design — the base of the pyramid shape following the line of the figure's forearms and folded hands.

The Last Supper is another one of Leonardo's famous works. It pictures Jesus with the twelve apostles just after He has announced that one of them will betray Him. The placement of the men in the painting gives the scene a realistic sense of movement. This mural was painted quickly on moist plaster with paint whose colors are ground up in a limewater mixture. Leonardo, however, wanting to work slowly and revise his work, did much experimenting with compounds and paint mixtures. Unfortunately, the paint began to flake away and *The Last Supper*, housed in the convent of Santa Maria della Grazie in Milan, is in poor condition.

In the paintings by Leonardo da Vinci we see not only the work of a great artist but the work of one who understood anatomy, in the rendering of graceful hands or a turned head. We see the work of one who appreciated botany, in the careful and exact drawings of flower petals, leaves, and stems. We see the work of one who excelled in architecture in the detailed drawings of windows or ceilings or entire buildings in the landscape. Most of all, we see the wondrous work and knowledge of one who loved to create.

Name: _____

LEONARDO DA VINCI

VOCABULARY: Renaissance, portrait, contrast, observe, invention

MATERIALS: large colored paper, white paper, paint, paintbrush, pencils, stapler, crayons.

ACTIVITIES:

1. Study the sketches of objects and inventions that Leonardo da Vinci drew in his notebook. Make a notebook of your own by stapling white paper inside a large sheet of colored paper. Decorate your cover. Like Leonardo da Vinci, observe an object very carefully, then sketch it in your notebook. Create one or more inventions of your own to sketch.

2. Study Leonardo's paintings. Observe the blurred backgrounds in some of his paintings such as in his portrait of *Mona Lisa*. Also observe the contrasts of dark and light colors in his paintings. Paint a picture with a blurred background and with dark and light colors for contrast.

3. Write a poem or story about your piece of art.

Evaluation   Name: _____

THINKING ABOUT LEONARDO DA VINCI AND ME

Respond to four or more of the following questions/statements:

1. Name the two paintings by Leonardo da Vinci that are considered among the most famous pictures ever painted.

2. What kind of design did Leonardo da Vinci sometimes use to organize his paintings? Where did he use this design in the painting of Mona Lisa?

3. Leonardo da Vinci wrote some of the notes by his sketches backwards and put them in front of a mirror to read. Why do you think Leonardo wrote his notes by his sketches backwards?

4. Do you think you have become a better observer by first viewing and then sketching various people and/or objects in your art notebook? Explain.

5. Write a description of your favorite sketch or invention that you drew in your art notebook.

6. Write one or more paragraphs about what you have learned about this artist and/or what you have learned through your own creative project relating to this artist. Write this information on the opposite side of this sheet or on a separate sheet of paper.

Paul Gauguin
(go GAN)
1848–1903

Paul Gauguin was a French Post-Impressionist artist who became famous for his decorative paintings which were created using large blocks of flat, expressive colors and strong, simple outlines. The people of Tahiti and their legends and landscapes were often the subject of some of his most impressive work. Paul Gauguin's early work was influenced by the French painters Camille Carot and Camille Pissarro and, in turn Gauguin's paintings served as inspiration to the Fauves, a group of French artists including Vincent Van Gogh, Paul Cézanne, Georges Rouault, and the German expressionists working in the early twentieth century.

Eugene Henri Paul Gauguin was born in Paris, France on June 7, 1848. His father was a journalist and his mother was the daughter of the famous writer Flora Tristan. Young Paul spent his early childhood in Peru, his mother's homeland, but returned to France to go to school when he was seven years old. When he was seventeen years old he went to sea as a sailor in the merchant marine. After six years at sea, Gauguin decided to pursue a career in banking instead, and became a very successful stockbroker in a Paris bank. In 1873 he married Mette Sophia Gad, the daughter of a Danish minister, and they had five children.

Gauguin's interest in painting and collecting art increased after his marriage and at the age of thirty-five, after the banking industry suffered a depression, he decided to devote himself entirely to art. Gauguin's first painting teacher and his closest friend, Emile Schuffenecker, encouraged him to pursue art and later even opened his home to Gauguin when he had no money to pay his rent.

Because he had difficulty supporting himself and his family, Gauguin had to move his wife Mette and their five children to Copenhagen, Denmark, his wife's homeland. Gauguin returned alone to France, living for a short period with the peasants in Brittany. He wanted to paint the simple pure life of the country people he admired. In Brittany, Gauguin met the artist Emile Bernard and together they embraced a philosophy and style of art that became know as synthetism. All the qualities of synthetism—simplified form, bold color, extreme shapes, and decorative efforts—are reflected in Gauguin's later works.

Initially, Gauguin joined the Impressionists, a group of highly creative nineteenth century painters who developed new techniques of painting. The Impressionists used short brush strokes of bright color to evoke certain moods and impressions. Gauguin exhibited with the Impressionists from 1880 to 1886. Among the Impressionists were Camille Pissarro, Edgar Degas, and Vincent van Gogh who became Gauguin's friends. Eventually the Impressionists broke up as each artist individually pursued his own highly personal and unique style. Vincent van Gogh invited Gauguin to live and paint with him in Arles, France, and Gauguin's striking painting *Landscape at Arles* was painted during this period. Van Gogh and Gauguin shared a great admiration for the work of the Japanese woodcut artists Hiroshige and Hokusai and both van Gogh and Gauguin's own works show the influence of these Japanese artists. Gauguin admired the simple way of life portrayed in Hiroshige's and Hokusai's art and sought a peaceful and simple way of life for himself.

Gauguin tired of European life, set sail for Tahiti. Gauguin admired the honesty and simplicity of the Tahitian people and their pure and primitive lifestyle. He stayed there and painted for two years, returning to France in 1893. But in 1895 he moved to Tahiti permanently.

With bold and dazzling colors, heavy, dark outlines, and large simplified shapes, Gaugin painted his lush surroundings. His largest and perhaps most famous painting measures, 4' 3 1/4" x 12' 3 1/2" and hangs in the Museum of Fine Arts in Boston. This painting is entitled, *Where Do We Come From? What Are We? Where Are We Going?* The brilliantly colorful oil painting depicts a calm and peaceful South Pacific setting with standing and resting figures looking serene and contemplative. All of Gauguin's later paintings reflect an aura of contentment, perhaps suggesting Gauguin's own happiness in the work he pursued. This gentle and dream-like quality is especially evident in Gauguin's exotic tropical paintings.

In 1901 Gauguin moved to the Marquesas Islands after a period of serious illness. There he died of leprosy on May 8, 1903. Paul Gauguin became famous not only for his paintings but for his masterful works of ceramics, woodcuts, and sculpture as well. Whatever form of art he pursued, Paul Gauguin expressed himself simply, directly, and powerfully.

Name: _____

PAUL GAUGUIN

VOCABULARY: geometric, effect, synthetism

MATERIALS: paints, crayons, chalk, oil pastels, or colored pencils.

ACTIVITIES:

1. Study the various styles of Paul Gauguin. Choose one of Gauguin's styles, such as the one above, to make a picture of your own. Although Gauguin usually painted his pictures, you may use whatever medium that is available to you.

2. After looking at *Still Life With Three Puppies* by Paul Gauguin, make your own picture using a specific geometric form such as a triangle, circle, cone, rectangle, or square, that can be repeated numerous times in your picture. Write a title for your picture on the front or back of the paper.

3. Write a description or a story about your picture.

Name: _____

THINKING OF PAUL GAUGUIN AND ME

Respond to four or more of the following questions:

1. Write the title of the picture that you made for the activity and explain why you chose this title.

2. What colors did you use in your picture? Why did you choose these particular colors?

3. If you could have talked to Paul Gauguin, what three questions would you have asked him about his work?

4. Write five sentences that describe Paul Gauguin and his work?

5. Paul Gauguin worked on the island of Tahiti in the South Sea Islands. After you have located these islands on a map, draw and label them below.

6. Write one or more paragraphs about what you have learned about this artist and/or what you have learned through your own creative project relating to this artist. Write this information on the opposite side of this sheet or on a separate sheet of paper.

Francisco Goya
(GOY ah)
1746–1828

Francisco Goya was perhaps the best-known Spanish painter and engraver of the eighteenth century. He was also one of the most important artists working in Europe. Goya became famous for his realistic portraits, particularly those of the royal Spanish court, and he eventually became the portrait painter of King Charles II and King Charles IV of Spain.

Francisco Goya's full name was Francisco José de Goya y Lucientes. He was born in a small town called Fuendetodos, near the bustling city of Saragossa, in 1746. When he was twelve years old, his parents moved their family to Saragossa, Spain and there Goya saw his first great works of art in many of the Saragossa churches. Later, one of Goya's first major commissions would be to paint frescoes in the Aaragossan Cathedral.

José Luzán, a painter who had studied in Naples, Italy, was the master artist in Saragossa during Goya's adolescence. When it became apparent to Goya's school teachers that he had a great interest and talent in art, the teachers sent him to José Luzán, with whom Goya studied for four years. In 1771 Goya traveled to Rome, Italy to study the great works of art found there.

In 1774, Goya began working as a painter to the Royal Tapestry Works in Madrid. A tapestry is a richly colored hand or machine woven fabric displaying a design or a picture. Goya did a series of more than fifty elegant and intricate designs for the Royal Tapestry Works. The designs were so beautiful and popular that the wealthy and royal members of Spanish society asked him to paint their portraits.

Goya painted many portraits of people which showed not only what they looked like, but what their personalities were like as well. In his portrait of King Charles III, displayed in the Museo di San Martino in Naples, Italy, Goya shows a gentle and friendly looking man, with his hunting dog curled at his feet. Later Goya painted the portraits of King Charles IV and his family, and because he did not like King Charles IV as well as he did King Charles III, Goya emphasized the royal family's coarse and dull features.

One of Goya's most famous portraits is a painting of a young boy, the son of a Spanish count, dressed in a bright red suit. The portrait, displayed in the

Metropolitan Museum of Art in New York City, is an oil painting on canvas entitled *Don Manuel Osorio Manrique de Zuniga*. The calm face of the dark haired little boy, Manuel Osorio, looks startlingly realistic. The boy is holding the leash of his pet bird as two cats in the background stare hungrily at the bird. The bird holds a piece of paper between its beak upon which Goya has signed his name.

Goya became a member of the Spanish Royal Academy of Fine Arts in 1780 when he was becoming Spain's most successful artist. Fifteen years later, when he was serving as principal painter to the Spanish court, Goya became president of the Spanish Royal Academy. His pleasant looking works at this time reflected his happy and peaceful state of mind.

In 1792, when Goya was only 42 years old, he became seriously ill and as a result of his illness lost his hearing. At this time Goya's work became more imaginative and mysterious, his brush strokes much freer and looser. Several of the paintings Goya completed after his illness have an impressionistic flavor that suggests a greater freedom of movement than his earlier works. This relaxed and expressive style led many to consider Goya a forerunner of the Impressionistic movement of the late nineteenth century — a style which later influenced the painting of the French artist Edouard Manet.

Goya produced his most effective religious paintings in the 1790s. When Napoleon Bonaparte, a famous French general, invaded and occupied Spain from 1808 to 1813, Goya produced a series of very powerful paintings including *The 2nd of May* and *The 3rd of May*, and engravings such as *The Disasters of War*, depicting the horrors of war.

In 1820, Goya retired to his country home called Quinta del Sordo, (House of the Deaf Man). He continued to paint very imaginative and sometimes extremely violent pictures that, perhaps, expressed the nightmares and visions he experienced after his illness. In his very dark and somber pictures Goya may have been expressing his fear and outrage of the war and the political turmoil occurring in his homeland. In 1823, only three years after retiring to his country home, and fearing for his safety, Goya moved to Bordeaux, France, where he continued to produce dazzling paintings until he died at the age of eighty two.

FRANCISCO GOYA

VOCABULARY: portrait, masterpiece, facial expression, signature, background

MATERIALS: paper, pencil, paints, brushes.

ACTIVITIES:

1. Read about Goya's work. Since you will be making a portrait, observe his portraits very carefully.

2. If possible, look at a photo of the painting, *Mauel Osorie Manrique de Zuniga.* See the bibliography in the back of this book to find out where to locate a picture of this painting. Notice how the child seems to stand out from the background and notice how realistic the boy looks. What animals do you see in the picture and what do they look like they are going to do? What does the boy's facial expression tell us? Can you find Goya's signature?

3. Draw your self-portrait or a portrait of another person. Practice sketching the portrait before you do your final one. You might want to include some animals and/or objects in your picture. Perhaps, like Goya, you will include your signature in a special place in your picture.

4. Write a story, poem, or description of your creative piece of art.

Evaluation   Name: _____

THINKING ABOUT FRANCISCO GOYA AND ME

Respond to four or more of the following questions/statements:

1. Did you make a self-portrait or a portrait of someone else? Why? Did you include any objects or animals in your picture?

2. Which of Goya's paintings that you studied do you like best? Why?

3. What did you find the most difficult about making a portrait?

4. How does the person in your portrait feel? Do you think that you made the person look the way he/she feels?

5. If you used other objects in your picture, describe the meaning of them and why you chose those particular objects/animals.

6. Write one or more paragraphs about what you have learned about this artist and/or what you have learned through your own creative project relating to this artist. Write this information on the opposite side of this sheet or on a separate sheet of paper.

Katsushika Hokusai
(HO koo si)
1760–1849

Katsushika Hokusai was perhaps the most influential Japanese landscape painter of the nineteenth century. In addition to the works of Ando Hiroshige, another Japanese painter (1797–1858), Hokusai's landscapes represented the essence of Japan for many of his contemporaries. Hokusai also designed wood block prints, another popular, but less expensive, art form of the seventeenth, eighteenth, and nineteenth centuries. These prints were made after an expert engraver placed an artist's drawing on a piece of wood and cut lines which followed the pattern of the drawing into the wood. The wood block cut was printed only in black. Then the artist colored in the print. After this initial coloring more blocks were made, one block for each color used. Each block was then printed on top of the other. Hokusai was a prolific printmaker, making thirty thousand drawings. From 1823 to 1835, Hokusai created a series of prints, the most famous series consisting of various scenes of Mount Fuji, the highest mountain in Japan, located on Central Honshu Island.

Katsushika Hokusai was born in Edo (now Tokyo), Japan in 1760. Even though he began drawing when he was only six years old, he felt that he did not truly learn how to draw well until he was in his sixties. He produced most of his important work after he was sixty. Hokusai was a very modest man and felt that he had not produced anything satisfactory until he was seventy.

Hokusai studied under a leading Japanese artist, Katsukawa Shunsho. Although Hokusai created an enormous amount of paintings and prints, varying his technique and style, he is most famous for his landscape prints. Hokusai had a highly decorative and dramatic style of drawing and used heavy, bold lines to emphasize the shapes of his subjects. Hokusai favored the colors brown, blue, and green. Even though Hokusai's prints were extremely popular, and most of them sold the day they were published, Hokusai lived most of his life in poverty. After his death in 1849, some of his prints were displayed in Europe where years later, in the 1800s, they had a profound impact on the Post-Impressionist painters Vincent van Gogh, Paul Gauguin, and Henri de Toulouse-Lautrec.

In two of Hokusai's prints, both found in the British Museum in London, his wonderfully structured scenes and decorative, abstract style is evident. These two-color wood-block prints, *Fuji Seen Through the Waves off Kanagawa* and

Ono Waterfall, demonstrate Hokusai's skill at combining color and form to present a vividly dramatic scene. In *Fuji Seen Through the Waves off Kanagawa,* from a series called *Thirty-Six Views of Mount Fuji,* the focus of the painting is a large, curling wave lifting dangerously over small fishing boats. In *Ono Waterfall,* the focus of this landscape print is on the bold lines and dramatic height of the waterfall as a group of onlookers gaze at it from below.

Katsushika Hokusai was the master of the Japanese color print. His contribution to the art world and his influence upon Western artists remains a remarkable and outstanding accomplishment.

Name: _____

KATSUSHIKA HOKUSAI

VOCABULARY: landscape, foreground, background, middle ground, compare, contrast

MATERIALS: pictures of various landscapes and outdoor scenes, paper, and various kinds of media such as paints, colored pencils, chalk, and crayons.

ACTIVITIES:

1. Observe and discuss a variety of landscape pictures including at least one by Hokusai. Compare these landscape pictures.

2. Like Hokusai you will have the opportunity to create a landscape picture. Observe the trees as well as other scenery around you. You may want to sketch some scenes before you decide on the one you want to paint or color.

3. Create and paint or color a landscape scene that is in your own neighborhood.

4. Write a description of your landscape for someone who will not be able to see it.

Evaluation   Name: _____

THINKING ABOUT KATSUSHIKA HOKUSAI AND ME

Respond to four or more of the following questions/statements:

1. Where did many of Hokusai's landscapes exist? Where does your landscape pictures exist?

2. What did you enjoy most about making a picture of a landscape? Do you plan to make another picture of a landscape soon? Why?

3. How did you make some items appear to be in the foreground and others appear to be in the background?

4. What was the most and least difficult task in making your picture?

5. Write a description of your landscape picture for an imaginary museum catalog.

6. Write one or more paragraphs about what you have learned about this artist and/or what you have learned through your own creative project relating to this artist. Write this information on the opposite side of this sheet or on a separate sheet of paper.

Edward Hopper

1882–1967

Like the nineteenth century Post-Impressionist French artist Henri Rousseau, Edward Hopper did not concentrate fully on painting until he was over forty years old. Today the American Edward Hopper is recognized as the most important realist painter of the twentieth century. Edward Hopper painted everyday subjects, finding beautiful simplicity in gas stations, country roads, city buildings, highways, railroads, bridges, houses, restaurants, and movie theatres. Like one of his great contemporaries, Norman Rockwell, Hopper chose to honestly render on canvas the older, weathered neighborhoods he found so irresistible as subject matter. Through these everyday subjects Hopper managed to convey a sense of loneliness and isolation, even when he included people in his paintings.

Edward Hopper was born in Nyack, New York, in 1882, but for most of his life he lived in New York City where he received many of the ideas for his paintings from his surroundings. His mother encouraged both Edward and his sister, Marion, in their drawing as it was one of the children's favorite pastimes. Because Edward grew up along the Hudson River in New York City, he drew many pictures of the water and the boats on it. *The Long Leg*, an oil painting done in 1935, pictures an isolated sailboat not far from the shore. The painting is dominated by varying shades of blue and there is a quiet sense of calm and solitude about the painting. In an earlier painting entitled *Sailing* (1911), Hopper used both design and large unbroken areas of color to emphasize the isolation of the sailboat and its two occupants far away from land. The stark realism in both paintings is a distinguishing characteristic of Hopper's work.

After graduating from high school, Hopper's parents sent him to New York City to study art. He learned a great deal about art from a teacher named Robert Henri. Henri believed there was beauty in shabby city buildings, factories, and highways. Hopper liked Henri's ideas and found very interesting things to paint in scenes and subjects that we might see every day even now. After art school Hopper traveled to Paris, France, several times and studied painting there. When he returned to New York, he worked as a commercial artist and illustrator. When he wasn't working at his job as an illustrator, he painted, mostly during his summer vacations in Maine. In 1913, he sold his painting *Sailing* at the New York Armory Show, a famous art exhibition attended by four hundred thousand people.

After the Armory Show, Hopper didn't sell many of his paintings so he began making etchings, a kind of printing done on metal plates. He achieved some renown with them. Then in 1924 Hopper had his first one-man exhibit. It was very successful and afterward Hopper began creating the stark, melancholy paintings for which he is most famous.

Hopper and his wife, Jo Nivison, also an artist, enjoyed driving along country roads in New England, looking for subjects of inspiration. Hopper was very interested in patterns of light and shade and he studied his subjects carefully, shaping particular areas geometrically and deleting distracting details.

One of his most famous paintings, *Nighthawks*, done in 1942, hangs in the Art Institute of Chicago. Even though there are people in the lighted diner, the place looks empty and lonely. There is a stillness about the painting that suggests power and mystery.

Hopper's unusual view of ordinary subjects made for extraordinary paintings, making him America's foremost realist painter.

Name: _____

EDWARD HOPPER

VOCABULARY: ordinary, composition, shadow, surface, three-dimensional

MATERIALS: Pictures and photos of real buildings, small and large sheets of various colors of construction paper including green for grass and yellow for light bulbs, scissors, glue, paint, crayons, colored pencils, markers.

ACTIVITIES:

1. Observe various buildings around your town. Sketch the buildings on a sheet of paper.

2. Like Edward Hopper, notice how the light shines inside the buildings and how it shines on and near them. Also notice the various shadows on and near the buildings. Try to discover what makes these shadows.

3. Although Edward Hopper painted mostly on flat surfaces, your project will become a three-dimensional project. Fold and crease your paper to represent a building as seen in the illustration above. Paint or color your paper to represent a building. After your work is completed stand your building up to display it. Make a sidewalk or yard to place in front of the building. Will some shadows show on this part of your scene? A street light might be made by dipping a straw in glue and then placing it on the ground paper, perhaps on a street corner. A yellow light bulb can be made from a yellow scrap of paper and glued to the top of the straw.

Evaluation   Name: _____

THINKING ABOUT EDWARD HOPPER AND ME

Respond to four or more of the following questions/statements:

1. Write the name of the city and state where Edward Hopper was born. Locate it on a map.

2. Why do you think Edward Hopper enjoyed painting ordinary things?

3. Write the names of at least six ordinary things you would like to paint sometime.

4. Write the titles of at least three of your favorite photos and/or pictures that you have studied by Edward Hopper. Underline the title of the one you like best.

5. If you were to travel as an artist like Edward Hopper, what two places would you like to visit and what would you paint there?

6. Write one or more paragraphs about what you have learned about this artist and/or what you have learned through your own creative project relating to this artist. Write this information on the opposite side of this sheet or on a separate sheet of paper.

Paul Klee
(clay)
1879–1940

Paul Klee, one of the most original masters of modern painting, was greatly inspired by children's drawings. His own vivacious and brightly colored drawings, paintings, and watercolors often have a fairy tale quality to them. Klee, like the Russian artist Marc Chagall (1887–1985), was influenced by the works of the Cubists. Cubism, a revolutionary new art form born at the beginning of the twentieth century, created new forms and geometric shapes that had not been represented in the art world before. Klee created a variety of whimsical and imaginative symbols and objects to show how to look beyond the surface to get to the true heart of things.

Paul Klee was born near Bern, Switzerland, on December 18, 1879. As a child, Paul loved to draw, as did his mother, and he loved to draw cats, which were his favorite pets. His favorite cat was Bimbo. When Paul Klee was a grown man he had a favorite tiger tomcat named Fritzi. As an adult Klee paid tribute to his cat and the cat's wild hunting instinct in a painting entitled *Cat and Bird* (1928). With the beautiful and vivid colors Klee became famous for using, he painted a red heart-shaped nose on Fritzi showing his fondness for his cat. Between Fritzi's large bright green eyes rests a bird, the subject of Fritzi's hunt. The close-up portrait of the cat radiates great warmth and vitality with its range of reds and greens, and a small amount of black and white. *Cat and Bird* hangs in the Museum of Modern Art in New York City.

Paul Klee's German parents fostered his love not only for drawing but for music as well. Klee's mother was a singer and his father was a music teacher. Both taught Paul how to play the violin when he was a young child. When Paul became older he played with the Bern Municipal Orchestra, and he continued to play with them even after he had completed art school.

In 1906 Klee married and moved to Munich, Germany, which was a very important art center at the time. Many artists lived and worked there at the beginning of the twentieth century, experimenting with various forms and techniques, and mastering new art styles that no one had ever seen before. In Munich Klee became friends with the artists Wassily Kandinsky, August Macke, and Franz Marc. These artists presented abstract forms in bright colors and unusual shapes; their work inspired Klee and helped him realize that paintings did not have to look like photographs. Klee realized there were new and exciting worlds to explore in art if one looked beyond the surface of things.

In 1914, Klee traveled to Tunisia in North Africa with his friend, the artist August Macke. In Tunisia Klee marveled at the clear light and beautiful color. The light and color in this mysterious and exotic country had a profound effect on Klee, prompting him to declare in his diary, "Color and I are one. I am a painter..." Klee painted many watercolors of what he saw in Tunisia. Displayed in the Museum der Stadt in Ulm, Germany, is a watercolor painting showing a range of earth colors entitled *Kairouan*. In the painting Klee has drawn the shapes of Tunisian buildings along the horizon.

A sense of great energy or movement is evident in many of Paul Klee's paintings. Because Klee wanted his viewers to experience new thoughts and feelings inspired by his unusual depiction of some traditional subjects, he constantly experimented not only with forms, shapes, and colors, but with painting materials and painting surfaces as well. In the watercolor *Ab Ovo* (1917), the rough edges of the cloth Klee painted on. And in an oil painting entitled *Senecio* (1922) one can imagine feeling the rough, uneven texture of the oil paints on the canvas. Some of Klee's paintings even give the viewer the sensation of vibrating music. The watercolors *Fugue in Red* and *Crystal Gradation*, both painted in 1921, seem to emit a great sense of musical energy as their many abstract shapes and forms appear to vibrate.

Near the end of his life Paul Klee used darker colors and more serious titles for his works. He did not however, abandon the fantasy and magic that highlighted his paintings and made him one of the foremost masters in the modern art world.

PAUL KLEE

VOCABULARY: abstract, images, sketch, symbol

MATERIALS: paper, paints and/or another kind of media.

ACTIVITIES:

1. Study some of the works by Paul Klee, including some of his abstract art. Since Paul Klee is known for his abstract art, you will have the opportunity to work with an abstract project too. Look for objects and symbols to use in your project; create images in your mind to help you get ideas and sketch them on paper. Then choose the one you like best for your abstract design and make a painting of it.

2. After you have completed your painting write a paragraph or more to show how you got your idea for your art. Write down any additional comments that you would like to share about your project.

Evaluation

Name: _____

THINKING ABOUT PAUL KLEE AND ME

Respond to four or more of the following questions/statements:

1. Write the name of the city and the country where Paul Klee was born and locate it on a map.

2. Write a paragraph describing one of Klee's paintings that you have studied. Write as clearly as you can so that your classmates/family will able to identify the painting when they read your paragraph or listen to your description.

3. Write three questions that you would like to ask Paul Klee if he were alive today.

4. Which of Paul Klee's paintings do you think is the most interesting? Why?

5. What would you do the same, and what would you do differently, if you could do your project of a Klee-type painting over again? Explain.

6. Write one or more paragraphs about what you have learned about this artist and/or what you have learned through your own creative project relating to this artist. Write this information on the opposite side of this sheet, or on a separate sheet of paper.

Michelangelo

1475–1564

Michelangelo was one of the greatest artists in history. During the Italian Renaissance he was acknowledged as a genius blessed with divine inspiration. While Michelangelo is best known for his grand and heroic marble sculptures, he was also a great painter, architect, and poet.

Michelangelo Buonarroti was born on March 6, 1475, in the Italian village of Caprese. After Michelangelo's birth, the family returned home to Florence. At the age of twelve Michelangelo became an apprentice to the well-known artist Domenico Ghirlandaio. Before he completed his apprenticeship, Michelangelo began sculpting under the guidance of a student of the sculptor Donatello. Soon Michelangelo's work attracted the attention of the ruler of Florence, Lorenzo d'Medici, who invited Michelangelo to work and study in his place. During this time Michelangelo began to study anatomy, a science very beneficial to his sculpting because it dealt with the structure of the human body.

By the time Michelangelo was twenty-three, he had gained great recognition as a sculptor. The larger-than-life marble statue that secured his reputation was the *Pietá*, a graceful yet strong figure of the mourning Virgin Mary holding Jesus Christ, her dead son, in her arms. The *Pietá* was completed between 1498 and 1499 and is now in St. Peter's Church in Rome.

After living in Rome for several years, Michelangelo returned to Florence where he met another artistic leader of the Italian Renaissance, Leonardo da Vinci. Because Leonardo and Michelangelo's talents were so widely recognized and admired, the government of Florence asked both artists to honor the city by painting battle scenes on the wall of the city hall. Although the project was never completed, Michelangelo nevertheless learned a great deal from Leonardo who taught him how to portray vibrant action and motion in his paintings.

Michelangelo could not complete the fresco paintings for Florence's city hall because he was summoned to Rome to complete a tomb for Pope Julius II, one of the greatest and most ambitious of the Renaissance popes and a generous benefactor of the arts and sciences. The Pope also wanted Michelangelo to paint the frescoes on the ceiling of the Sistine Chapel in the Vatican in Rome. The frescoes adorning the Sistine Chapel are regarded now as Michelangelo's finest achievement as a painter. While Michelangelo was seldom completely satisfied with his work, and often expressed his dislike concerning the Sistine Chapel project, the end result was, and is, enormously moving and breathtaking.

The frescoes on the Sistine Chapel ceiling show nine scenes from the Old Testament, including several scenes of God creating the world, the story of Adam and Eve, and the story of Noah and the Flood. Surrounding these scenes, Michelangelo painted the twelve Old Testament prophets and five sibyls, female prophets who foretold the figure. The larger-than-life figures convey great sensitivity and intelligence, strength and purpose. The figures in the scenes from the Old Testament are depicted with fluid and free movement, which Michelangelo was able to portray because of his work with Leonardo da Vinci.

The Sistine Chapel frescoes took three years to complete, after which, in 1511, Michelangelo resumed work on the Pope's tomb, carving three statues: one statue was of Moses and two others were of prisoners, figures often called *The Heroic Captive and The Dying Captive*. Then Michelangelo accepted several commissions from the ruling Medici family who had, by 1515, regained control of Florence. In addition to designing a chapel for the family, he designed and carved two famous tombs for the Medici princes, Giuliano and Lorenzo.

Michelangelo returned to Rome once more where he accepted a commission from Pope Clement VII to paint the altar wall of the Sistine Chapel in the Vatican. When Pope Clement VII died, his successor, Pope Paul III, urged Michelangelo to continue his work for the church. This work, a monumental fresco entitled *The Last Judgement*, is one of the world's greatest paintings and perhaps Michelangelo's most outstanding work of art. The huge fresco, fourteen meters high by thirteen meters wide, shows a mass of somber figures with Jesus Christ, in the upper center, judging those who have been good or bad and sending them, respectively, to heaven or hell.

Michelangelo's final paintings were frescoes for the Pauline Chapel in the Vatican, completed when he was seventy-five years old. Architecture and poetry absorbed much of his interest the last thirty years of his life. Michelangelo continued to create until he died at the age of almost ninety in Rome, on February 18, 1564.

Michelangelo, a leader in Italian Renaissance because of his work as painter, sculptor, architect, and poet, today remains one of the greatest artist of all time.

Name: _____

MICHELANGELO BUONARROTI

VOCABULARY: sculptor, sculpture, relief sculpture, representation, marble

MATERIALS: clay, plastic plate or bowl for the base or for the background of the sculpture, light-weight tagboard or a large sheet of paper for drawing, and crayons or sculptured markers

ACTIVITIES:

1. Michelangelo liked to make statues and relief sculptures of people. Choose a subject such as an animal, person, or a flower to create a sculpture of your own. After you have made your sculpture, place it on a plate or bowl that is turned upright or upside down to serve as a base, or use the plate for the background of a relief sculpture.

2. Create and draw a representation of your statue or relief sculpture on a large sheet of tagboard or paper. Cut out your sculpture and display it in some appropriate place.

3. Write a description, story, poem, or play about your piece of art.

Name: _____

THINKING ABOUT MICHELANGELO AND ME

Respond to four or more of the following questions/statements:

1. What do you think Michelangelo enjoyed most and least about creating his artwork?

2. What did you enjoy most and least about being a sculptor?

3. List three of Michelangelo's most famous sculptures. Which one is your favorite?

4. Where will/did you display your sculpture? If you were to sell your sculpture, where do you think the buyer should display it? Why?

5. Sketch and label at least three other sculptures that you would like to sculpt sometime.

6. Write one or more paragraphs about what you have learned about this artist and/or what you have learned through your own creative project relating to this artist. Write this information on the opposite side of this sheet or on a separate sheet of paper.

Louise Nevelson

1900–1988

By the time she was nine years old, Louise Berliawsky Nevelson knew she would become a sculptor. And by her fifties, her monumental award-winning sculptures were exhibited in several New York City museum collections. Louise Nevelson is perhaps most famous for the innovative set of sculptural forms she used, which included boxes, reliefs, columns, and walls. Initially many of her sculptures ore assemblages were grouped within boxlike frames and made from wood. To display a more unified and harmonious presentation of her art, Louise Nevelson often painted the sculptural pieces all black or all gold or later, in white.

Louise Berliawsky was born September 23, 1900, in Kiev, Russia. When she was four years old she and her family immigrated to America and settled in Rockland, Maine, where her father found work in the lumber and real estate business. During her youth, Louise was much taller than the rest of her classmates and partly because of that height difference, she felt awkward and shy. She was the captain of her basketball team and realized even then that she was destined for greater things.

Louise Berliawsky married Charles Nevelson in 1920 and moved to New York City where she studied painting at the Art Students League. In 1931 she continued her art studies in Munich, Germany, with the well-known teacher Hans Hoffmann. When she returned to her studies at the Art Students League in 1932, she again studied with Hoffmann in New York City. During this year she also worked with the great Mexican muralist, Diego Rivera.

In the 1930s Louise Nevelson became part of a growing clan of innovative artists. In 1933 she first exhibited in gallery group shows in New York. Then, her sculptures were small figurative pieces derived from Cubism and shaped in a variety of materials, such as wood, stone, plaster, and terra-cotta. Sometimes she would cast sculptures in metal. In the early 1940s, she created a group of wooden circus clowns and animals but later, dissatisfied, she burned them after they were exhibited.

In the 1950s her commanding and impressive pieces of sculpture reached new realms and explored new possibilities. The Whitney Museum in New York City acquired her piece *Black Majesty* in 1956 and thereafter other museums began to acquire her sculptures. In 1958 Nevelson created an eleven-foot-tall assemblage of wooden boxes, painted all in black. This wooden structure, *Sky Cathedral*, dramatically changed the way viewers regarded sculpture. The sweeping expanse of black and the sheer enormity of the sculpture projected a feeling of majestic calm which is often portrayed in Nevelson's work.

In the 1960s Nevelson began experimenting with a wider variety of materials such as plexiglas, aluminum, formica, and Cor-Ten steel. Nevelson's angular and massive work, *Transparent Horizon* (1975), at the Chemistry Building at the Massachusetts Institute of Technology in Boston, consists of black-painted Cor-Ten steel. Nevelson continued to create monumental environmental pieces made out of steel that framed the city landscapes of Boston, Cambridge, San Francisco, and New York. *Palace*, (1977) is a dazzling twelve-foot walk-in structure made of black-painted wood with a black-mirrored floor. It consists of a variety of black wooden shapes and forms tacked together to present a powerfully harmonious yet mysterious effect.

Louise Nevelson was a pioneer in the world of sculpture who sought harmony both in her art and in her personal life. She created many new and exciting ideas for sculpture at a time when sculpture was previously thought to have had certain limits and boundaries. Major museums in the United States, including the Whitney Museum in New York City, the Museum of Fine Art in Houston, Texas, and the Walker Art Center in Minneapolis, Minnesota have organized retrospectives of the work of Louise Nevelson.

Name: _____

LOUISE NEVELSON

VOCABULARY: collection, composition, values, plexiglas, shallow

MATERIALS: one big box top (depth of a shoe box top) or a large flat piece of cardboard, glue, throw-away such as wood, cardboard, plexiglas, plastic objects, or a margarine tub.

ACTIVITIES:

1. Study some of the works by Louise Nevelson.

2. Use either a large shallow box or a flat piece of cardboard as a background. Assemble a collection of throw-aways on your background. Think about their form and how they look next to each other. Think about the shadows and the shapes cast and the lights and the darks of your composition. Once you are satisfied with your assemblage, glue the pieces in place. You may paint them if you wish. You may want to make another project with objects that are very personal to you, such as things you enjoy collecting.

Name: _____

THINKING ABOUT LOUISE NEVELSON AND ME

Respond to four or more of the following questions/statements:

1. Observe a photograph of one of Louise Nevelson's sculptures. Then write your own thoughts about it.

2. Pretend you have a friend who cannot see. How would you describe your sculpture to this friend? Use as much detail as you can.

3. If you painted your sculpture, describe what colors you chose and why you chose them. If you chose not to paint your sculpture, explain why.

4. Look at your sculpture in an area where there is little light and then again where there is a lot of light. Describe what your sculpture looks like in both of these areas.

5. What did you think about as you created your sculpture?

6. Write one or more paragraphs about what you have learned about this artist and/or what you have learned through your own creative project relating to this artist. Write this information on the opposite side of this sheet, or on a separate sheet of paper.

Pablo Picasso
(pih KAH so)
1881–1973

Picasso. No other name in the world today is as synonymous with contemporary art as is Picasso's. Throughout his long and brilliant lifetime, Picasso created masterpiece drawings, paintings, etchings, sculptures, ceramics, lithographs, and collages. Whatever artistic medium Picasso attempted, he quickly mastered. Few artists have ever in their lifetime, achieved the worldwide recognition Picasso had. Picasso's innovative contributions to art are celebrated in countless museums all over the world.

Pablo Ruiz Picasso was born in Malaga, Spain, the night of October 25, 1881, to Doña Maria Picasso and Don José Ruiz Blasco. Following Spanish custom, the baby's first name was followed by his father's family name, then by his mother's family name. Pablo's father was a painter who was fond of painting traditional landscapes and still lifes of birds and flowers. Throughout Pablo's childhood his father taught art in various fine arts academies, and also gave young Pablo his first instruction in art. By the time Pablo was thirteen years old, his father knew that his son's artistic talents far surpassed his own.

In 1895 Pablo's father received a teaching position in the Fine Arts Academy in Barcelona, a city in northern Spain near the border of France. In Barcelona Pablo enrolled in the Academy and because he had already mastered many of the skills taught in the introductory art courses, he was allowed to attend the advanced courses. He skillfully and quickly completed his assignments. Because his artistic skills were already so outstanding, Pablo became bored with the subjects the Academy offered. Don José, Pablo's father, found a studio for his son where he could work independently. During this period Pablo produced paintings and drawings in a traditional style. Some of his subjects included a choirboy, a first communion, and a doctor visiting a dying patient.

When he was sixteen years old, Pablo left home for the first time, venturing to Madrid, Spain. He enrolled in the art school there but soon found his studies boring. He quickly discovered that the street life in Madrid — the gypsies, circus performers, and beggars — was much more fascinating than art school. The circus performers and the Spanish bullfights were subjects of lifelong interest to Pablo and he continually portrayed them in his work.

Picasso's work was constantly changing as he sought new ways to share his artistic visions and dreams. His continuous search for new ways of expressing himself, and his subsequent mastery of all that he attempted is what makes Picasso's contribution to the art world so inspiring and amazing. While Picasso was still living in Spain he pursued a style of painting marked by sad and lonely figures, often very poor and hungry people from the streets, painted predominantly in various shades of blue. Picasso's paintings during this three year time span fall into what is called his Blue Period. Later, the subjects of his paintings portrayed less melancholy moods and were depicted with warmer colors. This period of his work is sometimes referred to as his Rose Period because of the soft rose pink that dominated some of his paintings. Some have also called this period of work Picasso's Circus Period because many figures from the circus, which Picasso loved, were the subjects of his paintings. In his oil painting, *Family of Saltinbiques*, now in the National Gallery of Art in Washington, D.C., we see a family of circus performers quietly grouped together. The *Family of Saltinbiques* is the largest and perhaps the most important of Picasso's circus paintings.

In 1905 and 1906 Picasso again changed his style, based on his inspiration from the classical shapes of the Greek and Roman statues in the Louvre Museum in Paris. This period of painting would not be his only venture with classicism. In the 1920s he would return to it again.

In 1907 Picasso painted a single monumental work, *Les Demoiselles d'Avignon (The Girls of Avignon)*, which had an impact in the art world like no other painting before it. *Les Demoiselles d'Avignon* is an oil painting on canvas measuring 8' x 7' 8" and is on display at the Museum of Modern Art in New York City. This challenging painting depicts five monstrously large women, their figures angular rather than rounded and appearing almost three dimensional. The painting is radically different than his previous works because of its abstract, distorted forms. This painting style paved the way for the most revolutionary transformation in the art world since the Renaissance. From the painting style in *Les Demoiselles d'Avigon* Picasso moved on to collaborate with another artist, the Frenchman Georges Braque. They explored new ways of presenting reality, taking everyday objects and viewing them from different angles and perspectives. Together Picasso and Braque spearheaded the artistic movement known as Cubism, which characteristically portrayed dismantled geometric forms.

Pablo Ruiz Picasso, the leader and creator of abstract and contemporary art, remains one of the most famous painters of the twentieth century. He was an adventurer in the world of art, constantly exploring and defining new ways of seeing and learning. At the age of ninety-one, after a life passionately devoted to art, Picasso died at Le Mas Notre-Dame-de-Vie on April 8, 1973. In 1985 the Picasso Museum in Paris opened, housing the largest collection of Picasso's brilliant work.

PABLO PICASSO

VOCABULARY: painting style, Cubism, Classical Period, surface

MATERIALS: paints, colored pencils or crayons, markers, and paper.

ACTIVITIES:

1. Picasso enjoyed painting in various styles. Study some of his painting styles such as Cubism, his Blue Period, his Rose Period, and his Classical Period. Choose one of Picasso's styles for a picture you will draw or paint. Before you start your project, make some sketches for the picture that you have in mind. Draw or paint a picture about something that you find interesting. Perhaps you will get an idea from studying Picasso's work or from an experience you have had.

2. Artists "sign" their art work, sometimes in special ways. Find Picasso's signature on some of his works. Is there anything special about it? Remember to sign your work after it is completed.

Evaluation   Name: _____

THINKING ABOUT PABLO PICASSO AND ME

Respond to four or more of the following questions/statements:

1. Locate the cities and the countries on a map where Picasso was born and where he died. Then write the names of them below.

Picasso was born in _____

Picasso died in_____

Picasso lived from 1881 to 1973. How old was he when he died? _____

2. What style of Picasso's painting do you like best? Why?

3. If Picasso were alive today, what style do you think he might like best? Why?

4. Write a title for your painting and describe where you got the idea for the painting. Was it a special event? A special day? A friend or family member? A Picasso painting?

5. Picasso painted some of his paintings blue and some of his paintings rose. If you choose (or have chosen) to paint or color with one hue, which hue would you use? Why?

6. Write one or more paragraphs about what you have learned about this artist and/or what you have learned through your own creative project relating to this artist. Write this information on the opposite side of this sheet or on a separate sheet of paper.

Raphael
(raff ee EL)
1483–1520

One of the greatest artistic giants of the Italian High Renaissance was Raphael Sanzio, the son of a fairly successful court painter. Along with the sculptor Michelangelo, Raphael became one of the favorite artists of Pope Julius II.

Raphael, whose real name was Raffaello Sanzio, was born in Urbino, Italy, on April 6, 1483. Raphael received his early training from his father who was the court painter to the Duke of Urbino. When Raphael was eight years old, his mother died, and when he was eleven, his father died as well; however, shortly before his father died, young Raphael was taken to Perugia and apprenticed to the famous artist Pietro Perugino. In Perugino's workshop, Raphael learned many painting skills and was deeply influenced by his master's own sentimental style of painting.

In 1504, Raphael settled in France, the art capital of Europe at the time, and studied the works of the great Italian masters of the sixteenth century, Leonardo da Vinci and Michelangelo. Raphael used the faces of his admired teachers, friends, and fellow artists as models in some of his works. In one of the frescoes he painted for the Pope's private quarters in the Vatican, Raphael used the facial features of Leonardo da Vinci in his figure of the Greek philosopher Plato. In this same fresco, *School of Athens*, Italy's greatest sculptor, Michelangelo, is represented by the man writing on a stone block in the foreground of the painting. And Raphael's drawing of the famous Greek mathematician, Euclid, shares the facial features of Donato Bramante, Raphael's teacher and friend.

Raphael's *School of Athens* is one of the outstanding frescoes decorating the Stanza della Segnatura, one of the rooms in the Vatican Palace. This fresco has been considered the perfect embodiment of the classical spirit of the High Renaissance. Raphael was a master of color and form and in the School of Athens fresco we see figures, shapes, and colors all balanced gracefully and harmoniously with great dexterity and outstanding clarity.

School of Athens was completed in 1510, when Raphael's work was perhaps at its most mature. While his magnificent frescoes have achieved much acclaim, his portraits are known for their serenity and beauty. In his portrait *Unknown Woman*, also known as *La Muta*, done in 1507, Raphael displays not only his fine skill in capturing and conveying the quiet strength and dignity of a young lady seated for her portrait but also his mastery of a technique and formula implemented by his mentor, Leonardo da Vinci, in his famous portrait *Mona Lisa*. Raphael designed his portrait of *La Muta* so that the figure is architecturally inspired, following a pyramid shape. The pyramid design in a portrait was first put into effect by Leonardo da Vinci but Raphael, in *La Muta*, has successfully and originally reinterpreted it. One may wish to note the similarity of the crossed hands of each woman in Raphael's *La Muta* and Leonardo's *Mona Lisa*.

The position of the hands in Raphael's *Tempi Madonna* is also an important detail in this painting of a mother gently holding her baby. Raphael's most popular works were his *Madonna* (Virgin Mary) painting including the famous *Madonna della Sedia (Madonna of the Chair)* displayed in the Galleria dell' Accademia in Florence, Italy. In this painting we see a portrait of gentle demeanor, in soft rich colors, of a mother holding her child, while another child, hands clasped together, looks on.

Although Raphael's portraits are known for their serenity and beauty, his magnificent frescoes done for Pope Julius II have also achieved much acclaim. During Raphael's lifetime, the pope was the most powerful spiritual and political figure in all of western Europe. No one could compare with the Roman Catholic Church, and the head of the Church, the Pope, for enormous wealth and influence. During the Renaissance, vast amounts of work went into making the Roman Catholic churches and their properties the most magnificent and splendid monuments of the era. Thus it was important that Pope Julius II surrounded himself with the most highly regarded architects, painters, and sculptors of the time.

Raphael was commissioned by Pope Julius II to paint frescoes on the walls and ceilings of the Vatican's chapels and apartments. The Vatican Palace was, and is, the pope's residence within the city of Rome. After the important Italian architect, Donato Bramante, began work on St. Peter's Church in the Vatican, it was Raphael who continued to direct the construction of St. Peter's church after Bramante's death in 1514.

Raphael was certainly the most classic master of the High Renaissance and during his short lifetime, he died after a brief illness at the age of thirty seven, in Rome, he was acknowledged as a man of genius and one who had a tremendous impact upon future artists as well. More than three hundred years later, Raphael's classical serenity continued to greatly influence the nineteenth century French painters Jean Ingres and Auguste Renoir. Raphael died on April 6, 1520. A great architect as well, he was supervising the construction of St. Peter's Church in Rome and working on his last great work, *The Transfiguration*, before his death. His impact upon the future world of art could not have been foreseen in the sixteenth century, but to gaze upon his remaining works, it is not wonder.

Name: _____

RAPHAEL SANZIO

VOCABULARY: Renaissance, detail, perspective, proportion, space.

MATERIALS: paper, crayons, paints, pencils.

ACTIVITIES:

1. Raphael is a Renaissance artist well known for his attention to detail and his use of perspective, proportion and space. Read about and study some of the works by Raphael, paying special attention to his use of detail.

2. Make a picture using many details in it. Write a description about your detailed picture.

Name: _____

THINKING ABOUT RAPHAEL SANZIO AND ME

Respond to four or more of the following questions:

1. Explain what you like best about Raphael's artwork.

2. In what famous place did Raphael create many paintings on the walls and ceilings? This place is located in what city? Find it on a map.

3. How did you show perspective in your picture?

4. Where did you use the most detail in your picture?

5. List at least ten words or phrases that you associate with your picture.

6. Write one or more paragraphs about what you have learned about this artist and/or what you have learned through your own creative project relating to this artist. Write this information on the opposite side of this sheet, or on a separate sheet of paper.

Frederic Remington

1861–1909

Throughout his artistic career Frederic Remington was fascinated by the men, horses, and landscapes of the American West. Although he received little acclaim for his work during his lifetime, he remained faithful to his version of the Western frontier, as he created vivid and enduring images of the West, perpetuating its heroic and historic experiences.

Frederic Remington was fascinated by the people who faced the challenges of the rugged American frontier. He admired the courage and daring of explorers, cowboys, and American Indians, and he became famous for capturing their courage and spirit in over three thousand paintings and drawings and twenty two bronze sculptures. Frederic Remington, committed to chronicling the West as a writer as well as a painter. In addition to writing a novel and a Broadway play, he wrote 111 articles and stories and illustrated many of them including *Pony Tracks* (1895) and *The Way of an Indian* (1906). In his paintings, drawings, sculptures, and writings Remington brought an enduring and engaging vision of the West to many Americans who would never see it for themselves. Although Remington himself lived on the East Coast, he often traveled to Montana and the Dakotas, delighting in the landscapes and painting the adventures he imagined.

Frederic Remington was born October 1, 1861, in Canton, New York. He was a fine athlete and loved the outdoor life, spending much time swimming, fishing, and riding horses. Young Frederic also loved to draw and began sketching soldiers and battle scenes at an early age. Since Frederic deeply loved and admired his father, who was a former cavalry officer and hero in the Civil War, it is not unusual that his favorite drawing subjects were soldiers and horses. Although his parents did not object to Frederic's desire to pursue art as a career, they did not take his aspirations seriously.

Frederic attended the art school at Yale University but achieved more recognition as a football player than as an artist. His first published drawing, however, appeared in Yale's campus newspaper. After eighteen months at Yale, Frederic dropped out. In 1881 he left for Montana and worked as a cowboy and a wagon train hand before buying a sheep ranch in Kansas City. He also bought a saloon, and in 1884 married Eva Caten whom he had fallen in love with years earlier at a county fair. Eva disapproved of owning a saloon and chose to move back to New York. In the meantime, Frederic found himself penniless and felt that it was time to devote his life to art. Frederic returned to the East to join Eva but made frequent trips exploring the Northwest territory and the rapidly vanishing Western frontier. After his travels through the West he would return home to New York with sketches of soldiers, cowboys, American Indians and the grand, open lands of the West. In 1886 he began interpreting and illustrating the West for a number of leading magazines — by 1891 his art had made him famous.

Heroism, independence, and bravery are all values associated with Frederic Remington's finely detailed and precisely drawn works . Remington was interested in the struggle of an individual against overwhelming forces, whether they were animals, the weather, the land, or other individuals. Remington's action-filled canvases convey a great movement and power. Remington said that he not only wanted his audience to see the heat rising from horses as they rushed to battle, he wanted his audience to feel the heat as well.

In his later works, Remington became very interested in color and the effects of light. He used much looser and broader brush strokes and incorporated less detail. He painted some canvases in which the landscape was lit only by the moon and the stars. In his paintings, the composition, the color, and the balance of his subject matter, not only preserved his vision of the American West for his audience but also served as inspiration to many, including the great filmmaker John Ford who admired the action and movement in Remington's works and sought to duplicate them on film. Theodore Roosevelt also considered Remington a genuine artist and commissioned him to illustrate a series of articles.

In Remington's works, such as the painting *The Episode of the Buffalo Hunt* and the bronze sculpture *Bronco Buster*, the dramatic action and tension Remington became famous for capturing is clearly evident. In *The Episode of the Buffalo Hunt,* a charging bison collides with a surprised horse who tosses his rider, an Indian hunter, into the dusty air. *Bronco Buster*, Remington's first bronze sculpture, consisted of a traditional Old West subject, a cowboy atop his bucking horse. Remington had no formal training as a sculptor but worked very closely with the talented foundry craftsman, Ricardo Bertelli. Remington felt that the bronze sculptures perfectly expressed the action he sought to display. He created sculptures that ranged in height from twelve inches to twelve feet.

Only days before his death did Frederic Remington receive great praise and acceptance for his work. On December 4, 1909, Knoedler's Gallery of New York exhibited a series of Remington's *Nocturne* paintings. Great crowds attended the exhibit, declaring it a triumph. Unfortunately, Remington did not attend the opening because of his rheumatism. His health rapidly declined, complicated by appendicitis and an unsuccessful operation. On December 26, 1909, Frederic Remington died. He wanted his epitaph to simply declare: "He knew the horse."

FREDERIC REMINGTON

VOCABULARY: history, fascinated, challenges, frontier, observe

MATERIALS: paper, crayons or paints, stapler, newspapers and magazines such as *Time* and *Newsweek*.

ACTIVITIES:

1. Study Frederic Remington's works in encyclopedias and other books.

2. Frederic Remington was fascinated by the people who faced the challenges of the American frontier. He observed, wrote, and produced art works about some of the history that was being made at the time. Read newspapers and magazines to discover what is happening in your country. Like Remington, write and create pictures about some of the history that is taking place in your lifetime. After you have completed your pictures and writings, assemble these papers into a booklet as seen in the above illustration. At a designated time, share your booklet with others.

Name: _____

THINKING ABOUT FREDERIC REMINGTON AND ME

Respond to four or more of the following questions/statements:

1. Write the name of the city and state where Frederic Remington was born. Locate it on a map.

2. Write the title of Remington's artwork that you find most interesting and tell why you chose it.

3. Explain what you think is one of the most important contributions that Remington made to our society.

4. Look at some of Frederic Remington's sculptures and paintings. How are they alike? How are they different?

5. How did you decide on the subject matter for your own activity?

6. Write one or more paragraphs about what you have learned about this artist and/or what you have learned through your own creative project relating to this artist. Write this information on the opposite side of this sheet or on a separate sheet of paper.

Pierre-Auguste Renoir
(REN wahr)
1841–1919

Pierre-Auguste Renoir was one of the leading masters of Impressionist painting. Impressionism was a style of painting that was developed in the late nineteenth century. Some of the Impressionists, other than Renoir, were Claude Monet, Alfred Sisley, Camille Pissarro, and Paul Cézanne. These artists were fond of painting outdoors as they wanted to make the best use of natural light and to see the landscape and the colors of nature as they truly were. The impressionists used bright, bold dabs of color lightly and rapidly applied with short brush strokes. Their style of painting was loose and simply suggested objects and figures rather than concretely defining them. Because the Impressionistic style of painting was so vastly different from the style of painting that preceded it, the public did not receive their work warmly, at first. Renoir however, was one of the first Impressionists to be eagerly accepted by the public. His paintings were popular for their rich blend of colors and the gentle feelings they evoked. Renoir's favorite subjects were women and children and he often used his wife, children, and close friends as models.

Pierre-Auguste Renoir was born to a tailor and a dressmaker in Limoges, France, on February 25, 1841. When he was only fourteen, he was apprenticed to learn the art of painting porcelain dishes. To this day, Limoges, Renoir's birthplace, is famous for its delicately and beautifully hand-painted porcelains. Renoir displayed a strong and remarkable talent in drawing. When he moved to Paris in 1861, he painted fans and window shades, and by the time he was twenty he painted many murals on the walls of Paris cafes.

In 1862, Renoir enrolled at the École des Beaux-Arts, where he met Monet, Sisley, and Pissaro at the studio of Charles Gleyre. In 1874, these artists, along with Edgar Degas and Paul Cézanne, organized the original Impressionist exhibition, which was held in the studio of Paul Nadar, an important Parisian photographer of the day. This group of creative and innovative artists took their name from the title of one of Monet's paintings, *Impression, Sunrise*. The Impressionists were considered revolutionary as they abandoned the traditional Classical and Romantic conventions and instead embraced new ways of seeing and painting. In Monet's painting one sees an *impression* or suggestion of the subject (the sunset), rather than sharp and clear lines outlining the tightly focused subject.

Unlike several of the Impressionist painters, Renoir preferred painting figures rather than landscapes. One striking landscape scene, however, is captured in Renoir's painting entitled *L'Estaque*, which now hangs in the Museum of Fine Arts in Boston. Renoir and his friend and fellow artist, Paul Cézanne, often painted the scene which is immortalized on canvas *L'Estaque*. This was their favorite place to paint.

During the 1870s, Renoir received several commissions to paint portraits. One of his most famous portraits is entitled *Madame Charpentier and Her Children*. This graceful and richly colored painting hangs in the Metropolitan Museum of Art in New York City. Madame Charpentier, the subject of the painting, is dressed in a long black gown, seated on a sofa, and gazing gently in the direction of her two young daughters. Her two blonde daughters, about ages four and six, sit calmly beside their mother. The elder daughter is sitting on the family's large black and white dog.

Another famous Renoir painting is entitled *A Girl with a Watering Can* displayed in the National Gallery of Art in Washington, D.C. This richly colored portrait is of a little girl in a blue and white dress, a large red bow in her hair, holding a few flowers in one hand and a blue watering can in the other. Part of Renoir's strength in painting was that he was able to deftly place different shades of color side by side so that all the colors harmoniously complemented one another. In *A Girl with a Water Can* the striking composition of blues, greens, reds, and soft orange.

In 1880 Renoir traveled to Italy to explore and learn new techniques of painting. He became inspired by the works of the Italian Renaissance painter, Raphael, and a well-known Venetian painter of the eighteenth century, Giambattista Tiepolo. Upon returning to Paris, Renoir also learned much about artistic technique by studying the works of the French painters Eugene Delacroix (1798–1863), who represented the Romantic movement in painting, and Jean Ingres (1780–1867), who represented the Classical tradition.

Renoir continued to gain inspiration from the work of previous masters and he was constantly working to improve his own technique. Although Renoir is remembered for his paintings of happy, lively groups of people dancing, *Dance at Bouginal* in the Museum of Fine Arts, Boston; boating, *Oarsmen at Chatou* in National Gallery of Art, Washington, D.C.; or picnicking, *The Luncheon of the Boating Party* in the Phillips Collection, Washington, D.C.; he was in much pain from arthritis during the last years of his life. Despite the arthritis that crippled his hands he continued to paint by tying a brush to his hand; in this manner, Renoir developed a final painting style of bold colors and broad brush strokes.

PIERRE-AUGUSTE RENOIR

VOCABULARY: Impressionism, technique, apprentice, style, porcelain

MATERIALS: paper circles for fans, watercolors, crayons or colored pencils, colored chalk or markers, paper, and pencil

ACTIVITIES:

1. Renoir liked to draw and paint various objects and scenes in various styles. While he was in Paris, France, he painted window shades and fans. Like Renoir, make a fan. Fold your fan as seen in the directions above. Then unfold it and paint it. You will see by the creases where the fan will be refolded. Include the folds of your fan in your plan. After your paper is dry (if you have painted it), refold it to make a fan.

2. Write a story that includes your fan.

Name: _____

THINKING ABOUT PIERRE-AUGUSTE RENOIR AND ME

Respond to four or more of the following questions:

1. Write the name of the city and the country where Renoir was born. Locate it on a map.

2. If you could have spent a day with Renoir, what three things would you have liked to have done?

3. What Impressionist painting by Renoir do you like best? Why?

4. Observe a painting by Renoir for approximately three minutes. Write ten words and three phrases that relate to the painting.

5. Write some comments about your experiences with your fan project. Why did you choose the scene or design you painted?

6. Write one or more paragraphs about what you have learned about this artist and/or what you have learned through your own creative project relating to this artist. Write this information on the opposite side of this sheet or on a separate sheet of paper.

Diego Rivera
(rih VER ah)
1886–1954

More than one hundred years ago, deep in the mountains of Mexico in a small town called Guanajuato, twin sons were born to two proud parents. As infants, Carlos, and Diego, became very ill and Carlos died before he was two years old. In order to preserve Diego's health, his parents sent him to live with a nurse, an Indian healer, who treated Diego with special medicinal herbs. As Diego played in the fresh mountain air with the wild animals of the jungle he became stronger and healthier. When he finally returned home, Diego's parents celebrated his homecoming with a present of colored chalk. This seemingly small gift may have been the spark that ignited Diego's brilliant artistic talents, for Diego Rivera eventually became one of Mexico's most famous artists.

As a child, Diego loved to draw so much that his father made him a special room for drawing — a studio with walls lined entirely with chalkboards. Diego drew everywhere and anywhere and often his chalkboards were covered with playful and imaginative drawings of machines and mechanical inventions. These murals, which were large pictures painted or affixed directly on walls or ceilings, eventually became Diego's hallmark.

When he was ten years old, Diego entered the Academy of San Carlo in Mexico City to study with the leading academic painters of the time: Santiago Rebull, Felix Parra, José Salome Pina, and José Maria Velasco. Diego wasn't interested in drawing from models provided by the art school. Instead, he sought his inspiration from real life and he painted what he saw, both good things—people celebrating special occasions at the fiestas—and bad things—soldiers shooting down striking workers.

In 1907, when Diego was twenty-one years old, he went to study in Spain for one year. Then in 1911 he moved to Paris, the center of the art world, and became part of a group of artists and intellectuals who lived and worked in Montparnesse, a southern district in Paris on the left bank of the Seine River. From Paris Diego traveled to Italy for a year where he studied the murals and Renaissance frescoes inside the Italian churches. These frescoes (paintings which have been drawn on moist plaster surfaces with its colors ground up in a limewater mixture), fascinated Diego and had a great impact on his future work. Diego was also intrigued with the technique of fresco painting — a method that gave the paintings a long-lasting quality and made them more accessible to the public eye.

When Diego finally returned to Mexico in 1921 brimming full of ideas from his studies abroad, he began painting the first of eight major murals depicting historical subjects for the Mexican government. With Mexican artists José Clemente Orozco and David Alfaro Sigueiros, Diego experimented with fresco paintings and began to develop his own unique style of large, simplified figures and bold, brilliant colors. Diego's later murals told stories of Mexican peasants and their struggles to survive.

In 1929 Diego married Mexican artist Frida Kahlo who shared Diego's deep love for Mexican folk art and culture. Both artists worked in a style which reflected their passion for the native art of Mexicoz and its people. Although Diego's ideas influenced Frida's work, her paintings were small and very personal, unlike Diego's which were very large and public.

Diego's murals became very well known and many commissions, or special requests for his work, soon followed. In 1932, Diego and his wife Frida traveled to Detroit, Michigan, at the invitation of the director of the Detroit Institute of Arts who wanted Diego to create two large murals for the museum. Diego, who had been fascinated with machinery and industry since his childhood, enthusiastically accepted the offer to come and paint in a city so active in industrial process.

The *Detroit Industry* frescoes, as they came to be known, soon evolved into four murals on the east, west, north, and south walls showing the history of Detroit and the development of Detroit industry in the 1930s. The frescoes, which took eight months to complete, are the best examples of Mexican muralist work in the United States. Diego Rivera himself considered the Detroit Industry frescoes the most superior work of his career. In one of the panels he even included a self-portrait. Some of his other murals are in the National Palace in Mexico City and at the National Agricultural School in Chapingo near Mexico City.

If you are fortunate enough to visit and observe his murals, perhaps you will think about Diego Rivera, the young boy, who drew everywhere and anywhere with his chalk and who became one of his country's finest artists.

Name: _____

DIEGO RIVERA

VOCABULARY: mural, fresco, industry, labor

MATERIALS: large paper for mural (large grocery bags with the bottoms cut off work well for murals), paint and/or other media, paper, and pencil

ACTIVITIES:

1. When Diego Rivera was in the United States, he painted a mural for the Detroit Institute of Arts on the topic of science and industry. He enjoyed creating paintings which related to "work" because he thought work, or labor, was beautiful. What work do you find interesting and/or beautiful? Create a picture that relates to work. It might, for example, include yourself at work in the future, or it might include the equipment that you or other people might use in their work.

2. Write a story, play, or description about your mural.

Evaluation   Name: _____

THINKING ABOUT DIEGO RIVERA AND ME

Respond to four or more of the following questions.

1. Write the name of the city and the country where Diego Rivera was born. Locate it on a map.

2. Diego started drawing pictures when he was very young. What kind of pictures did you like to draw before you went to school? Sketch some of them on the back of this sheet of paper. How has your art changed since you were a preschooler?

3. Diego felt that labor was beautiful. What kinds of labor do you find interesting and/or beautiful? Explain.

4. Diego wanted people to have equality in work. What does "equality in work" mean to you? Explain.

5. If you were to make another mural, what would you do the same and what would you do differently? What topic might you choose for your mural? Why?

6. Write one or more paragraphs about what you have learned about this artist and/or what you have learned through your own creative project relating to this artist. Write this information on the opposite side of this sheet, or on a separate sheet of paper.

Norman Rockwell

1894–1978

Norman Rockwell, whose sentimental, and often amusing paintings graced the prestigious *Saturday Evening Post* for nearly half a century, remains one of America's best-loved artists.

Norman Rockwell frequently used his neighbors and friends as models while he painted the everyday happenings surrounding him. Rockwell is often considered a historian of a better era of America's past, a chronicler of happier times when small-town values and honesty were commonplace. Rockwell did not want to paint anything tragic or corrupt, he simply wanted to paint good-humored subjects. Norman Rockwell painted what he wanted life to be.

Norman Rockwell was born in New York City in 1894, to middle-class parents. He had one brother, and together they made their own entertainment. They often played baseball and although Norman's brother excelled at athletics, Norman did not. They shared a carefree, simple childhood, attending church on Sunday, and looking forward to riding the trolley car to the park. Their father read to them each evening, usually from one of Charles Dickens' stories. When Norman began to paint, his first subject was a Dickensian character.

Norman Rockwell's heroes were renowned and accomplished illustrators. After he studied at the Chase School of Art, the National Academy of Design, and the Art Students League, Rockwell's own illustrations appeared in popular periodicals such as *Boys Life*, *St. Nicholas*, and *American Boy*. In addition to these magazines he did illustrations for several others, as well as children's books. Rockwell was especially talented at capturing the youthful spirit of pre-adolescent boys pursuing their daily adventures. At the age of nineteen, Norman Rockwell had the good fortune of becoming the art editor of *Boy's Life* for which he illustrated the adventures and simple crises of young boys.

When Norman Rockwell was in his early twenties Clyde Forsythe, with whom he shared his studio, advised Rockwell to aim high in life if he wanted to be successful. Rockwell followed the cartoonist's advice and decided to submit two cover illustrations and a sketch for a third cover to the prestigious *Saturday Evening Post* which would be the best market for illustrators at the time. Rockwell presented his work to the art editor at the *Post*, Walter Dower, who not only bought both Rockwell's finished covers but asked him to finish the sketch for a third cover and commissioned him to develop three more covers. And so for the next forty-seven years, Norman Rockwell and The Saturday Evening Post shared one of the most famous working relationships in history.

Rockwell's first cover illustration for the Post appeared in May 1916. Entitled *Home Duty*, the illustration depicted a young boy, dressed in his Sunday best, pushing his baby sister in a carriage. The young boy looks very displeased with his task, especially as two other boys dressed in their baseball uniforms playfully tease him as they pass by.

Rockwell's covers for the *Post* not only increased the *Post's* readership (250,000 additional copies were printed when the issue had a Rockwell cover), but increased Rockwell's enormous popularity with the public. Rockwell was a very careful observer who possessed amazing technical skill. He could clearly envision how his large paintings would appear once they were sized down to a magazine or book format. Rockwell was not only able to perceive how his own work would "read" and duplicate, but he could create works that produced more powerful images after they were reduced. Rockwell's cover illustrations for the *Post* immediately seized the public's attention with its mix of warm colors and lively figures, creating scenes which captured and conveyed the honest small-town values that Rockwell himself represented. Not surprisingly, Norman Rockwell became, in his own quiet, unassuming way, a hero to the American public.

Among Norman Rockwell's most memorable paintings are the celebrated Post cover illustrations, *Breaking Home Ties* (September 25, 1954), depicting an eager young man bound for college waiting beside the tracks of a railroad station with his father; *Homecoming GI* (May 26, 1945), a very effective and sentimental painting illustrating the return home of a young GI from the war as his family and neighbors greet him; and *Marriage License* (June 11, 1955), a painting evoking great warmth and tenderness as a young couple applies for a marriage license before an elderly clerk who has probably witnessed this scene a thousand times before.

For the last twenty-five years of his life Norman Rockwell lived in Stockbridge, Massachusetts, where today the Norman Rockwell Museum exhibits the largest collection of original art by one of America's best-loved illustrators. Rockwell painted 324 covers for the *Post*. In addition to working for the *Post* and other major periodicals, he was commissioned to paint the portrait of every major presidential candidate from 1952 to 1972. Perhaps the best-known of Rockwell's creations are the *Four Freedoms* (1943), Rockwell's contribution to the war effort. After the *Four Freedoms* were published as a special supplement to the *Post*, the Office of War Information reproduced and distributed the series by the thousands. The paintings were then sent on a nationwide tour that raised over 132 million dollars in war bonds. Rockwell chose to illustrate these four freedoms as they applied to the United States. *The Four Freedoms* consist of *Freedom of Speech*, one of Rockwell's personal favorites, *Freedom to Worship*, *Freedom from Want*, and *Freedom from Fear* — perhaps the most convincing and effective of the Four Freedoms it shows a mother and father tucking in their sleeping children.

Norman Rockwell could create powerful paintings out of the simplest subject matter. He was adept at painting realistic facial expressions that conveyed a wide range of emotions, and the painstaking detail in all his work contributes to the overall mastery of his purely American subject matter. Norman Rockwell, the creator of some of the most endearing paintings in the United States, will always remain one of America's best-loved artists.

Activity Sheet   Name: _____

NORMAN ROCKWELL

MATERIALS: paper and pencil, copies of Norman Rockwell's work, various magazines with interesting covers, large sheets of construction paper to represent a magazine cover, crayons and/or markers.

ACTIVITIES:

1. Study various paintings by Norman Rockwell. Look at expressions on the faces of the people and animals. What do you think each person is saying or thinking? Where and when do you think he saw these people and animals? Choose one of Rockwell's illustrations that you think is interesting. Then write a story to accompany the illustration. You might make a sketch of your own about the story you wrote.

2. Examine and discuss various magazine covers designed by other illustrators. Think of a situation that would make an interesting picture for a magazine cover. Then design your own cover. Tell others how you came up with the idea for your project. Perhaps you will want to use your cover for a magazine that you design and write.

Name: _____

THINKING ABOUT NORMAN ROCKWELL AND ME

Respond to four or more of the following questions/statements:

1. What do you like best about Rockwell's work.

2. If you could purchase one print of Rockwell's work, which print would it be? Why would you choose it? Where would you hang it?

3. Write about something that happened to you that would make an interesting topic to illustrate.

4. What do you think is important for illustrators to think about before they illustrate a cover for a magazine?

5. Do you think you would be able to recognize some of Rockwell's other works when you see them? How?

6. Write one or more paragraphs about what you have learned about this artist and/or what you have learned through your own creative project relating to this artist. Write this information on the opposite side of this sheet or on a separate sheet of paper.

Henri Rousseau
(roo SO)
1844–1910

Henri Rousseau was a forty-year-old retired French customs official when he began painting full-time. He believed his life had not fully begun until he started to paint. Even when others criticized his work, Rousseau continued to have faith in his pursuits. Finally, just before Rousseau's death, his critics recognized the unusual and imaginative qualities in his work that made him the forerunner of early modern art.

Henri Rousseau was born in Laval, France, in 1844. Rousseau had received no formal art training. He was a self-taught painter and, therefore, he is sometimes referred to as a "primitive" painter. Rousseau always painted each detail in his pictures very lovingly and carefully. In many of Rousseau's paintings he included trees, his favorite subject, and each leaf of the tree was painstakingly represented. Rousseau was also very exact when it came to matching colors and sizes to the real life objects he was portraying on canvas. He often visited the zoo and botanical gardens in Paris to study the animals and plants. Rousseau would then use his new-found knowledge and his vivid imagination to create his own landscapes, such as his distinctive jungle landscape paintings which are particularly well-known.

Many of Rousseau's subjects pictured French middle-class life. Rousseau enjoyed painting portraits of his neighbors in their Sunday best as they rode in their carriages or took part in patriotic celebrations. Rousseau used very pure, clean colors and sharp outlines. He captured details — a strand of hair, a leaf on a tree — then he very precisely polished the surfaces of his canvas so that his paintings looked glossy, shiny, and bright.

Rousseau had a wonderfully vivid imagination and he loved to paint objects from worlds he fantasized about . Other artists drew great influence from some of the subjects in Rousseau's paintings, which look like they were inspired from mysterious and fantastic lands. Rousseau's painting *The Sleeping Gypsy*, displayed in the Museum of Modern Art in New York City, helped inspire the surrealism movement in the 1920s. The surrealism movement was a period when the style of art centered on very dreamlike or unreal characteristics. In *The Sleeping Gypsy* (1897) we see a wandering gypsy sound asleep clutching her walking stick. Her mandolin rests by her side as does a jar containing her drinking water. A lion sniffs the sleeping gypsy but does not harm her. The scene looks very peaceful and tranquil. There is a full moon in the upper right hand corner of the canvas and the midnight-blue sky is lit with a few bright stars, giving the picture a very poetic, solemn atmosphere.

In Rousseau's painting *The Dream* (1910) we encounter another enchanted, magical world. *The Dream*, also in the Museum of Modern Art in New York City, pictures a lush and peaceful jungle full of dense, green foliage, beautiful flowers, ripe fruit, exotic birds, lions, and an elephant. A lovely long-haired, woman, reclining on a bed, listens to a snake charmer standing in the center of the painting. Rousseau described the scene in the painting with a little poem he wrote:

> Yadwigha, peacefully asleep
> Enjoys a lovely dream:
> She hears a kind snake charmer
> Playing upon his reed.
> On stream and foliage glisten
> The silvery beams of the moon.
> And savage serpents listen
> To the gay, entrancing tune.

Henri Rousseau's innocent, imaginative paintings conveyed a quiet truth and beauty to those who viewed them. Pablo Picasso, the most famous twentieth century artist, paid homage to Rousseau, recognizing him as the forefather of modern painting.

HENRI ROUSSEAU

VOCABULARY: dominant, reveal, self-expression, create

MATERIALS: paints, brushes, paper and pencil

ACTIVITIES:

1. Find and study some pictures and/or photographs of Rousseau's work. Rousseau's favorite color was green. What are some objects he painted in green, or partly green?

2. Like Rousseau, paint a picture using your favorite color as a dominant color for your painting.

3. Rousseau enjoyed writing poetry, music, and plays. Write a poem, music, and/or a play about the piece of art that you created.

Name: _____

THINKING ABOUT HENRI ROUSSEAU AND ME

Respond to four or more of the following questions/statements:

1. What favorite color did you use in your picture? Why is this your favorite color?

2. Write the names of objects which you painted with your favorite color.

3. What did you enjoy most and least about making your picture?

4. Why do you think Rousseau sometimes painted imaginary animals instead of real animals in some of his works?

5. How is your picture similar to some of Rousseau's pictures?

6. Write one or more paragraphs about what you have learned about this artist and/or what you have learned through your own creative project relating to this artist. Write this information on the opposite side of this sheet or on a separate sheet of paper.

Rachel Ruysch
(roysh)
1664–1750

Artistically productive for nearly seventy years, Dutch still-life painter Rachel Ruysch was a woman of remarkable energy and talent. During a time when most women artists were trained either by their fathers or their husbands and were denied attendance at art academies simply because women were not formally and publicly educated before 1800, Rachel was apprenticed at the age of fifteen to Willem van Aelst, one of the greatest flower and still life painters of the seventeenth century. Her artistic gifts were encouraged by her father, a collector of scientific specimens and an amateur painter; and later by her husband, a portrait painter. Rachel Ruysch became the first woman to achieve international fame during her lifetime. Her flower paintings of beautifully detailed bouquets of roses, tulips, peonies, carnations, and poppies were sought by art patrons throughout Europe, thus making Rachel Ruysch a very wealthy woman.

Rachel Ruysch was born in 1664 in Amsterdam, Holland to parents who were prominent citizens in their community; her mother, Maria Post, was the daughter of the renowned architect Pieter Post; and her father, Anthony Frederick Ruysch, was a professor of anatomy and botany. His scientific collections of fossils, minerals, rare plants, shells, and skeletons likely prompted Rachel's interest in botany. Her skillful renderings of flowers and fruits, insects, reptiles, and small mammals clearly reveal her interest in both botany and zoology. One of Rachel's first dated works, completed, when she was eighteen years old, captures a study of insects and thistle plants on canvas. Another painting displays a composition of flowers and fruits. Ruysch's later compositions show the influence of the painter Otto Marseus van Schriek who emphasized dark landscape settings against which he placed particular specimens of plant and animal life. Although flower paintings dominated her work, Ruysch was also technically adept at painting groupings of fruits and insects, reptiles, and small mammals in landscape settings.

When she was twenty-nine years old, Rachel Ruysch married the portrait painter Juriaen Pool II. They had ten children. Despite all the responsibilities of her home and her children (most likely she had several servants to help her), Ruysch continued to be amazingly productive. There are sixty known signed and dated works by Ruysch as well as thirty-five works that are signed only. Rachel Ruysch was court painter to the Elector Palatine Johann Wilhelm von Pfalz, one of the German princes entitled to elect the emperor of the Holy Roman Empire, from 1708 until his death in 1716. While working for the Elector, Ruysch spent some of this time in his court in Düsseldorf, Germany. After the Elector Palatine's death, Ruysch settled her family once again in Amsterdam.

Rachel Ruysch, together with her contemporary Maria van Oosterwych, (1630–1693), was one of the finest flower painters in Holland in the late seventeenth and early eighteenth century. Her beautifully absorbing paintings are notable for their harmonious balance of flowers and fruits and for their graceful compositions of color, content, and design. Ruysch was also a master at suggesting movement in her flower arrangements, as if a gentle breeze had whispered past the swaying stems of flowers.

In her oil painting entitled *Still Life with Flowers and Plums* (1703), displayed in the Gemäldegalerie der Akademie der bildenden Künste in Vienna, Austria, Ruysch demonstrates her outstanding ability to create a beautiful, harmonious balance of flowers and plums. In the composition the forefront is dominated by the subdued colors orange-gold, cream, and rose, and we can see an arrangement of poppies, tulips, iris and other flowers against a very dark brown and green background. A draping stem of golden plums dominates the lower center of the painting and a ripe purple plum rests upon a ledge. If one looks closely, dragonflies, butterflies, a worm and an ant are also part of this lush display.

Another oil painting, *Flower Still Life*, part of the collection exhibited at the Toledo Museum of Art, depicts poppies and carnations bursting with brilliantly colored blossoms. Again there are several insects amidst the blossoms and two seashells placed near the vase of flowers. Originally, Ruysch painted a companion piece to *Flower Still Life*. We are aware of the companion piece because of an existing nineteenth century bill of sale. In this companion painting, a variety of fruits, a few flowers, a lizard, a bird's nest, and some insects graced the canvas. Ruysch did not paint many pairs of still life paintings because only her wealthiest clients could afford to buy them.

Rachel Ruysch actively painted until the last three years of her life. In her final paintings she not only signed her name and the date, but proudly added her age, "eighty three", as well. Her beautifully splendid bouquets of flowers and fruits remain ageless as admirers around the world continue to marvel at her work.

Name: _____

RACHEL RUYSCH

VOCABULARY: botany, still-life, detail, object, shade

MATERIALS: a large piece of paper for placemat, pencil, paint and brushes (or another medium), objects that will be represented in the picture, and laminating paper, clear adhesive paper, or waxed paper for protecting the placemat

ACTIVITIES:

1. Study Rachel Ruysch's work as well as still life pictures and photos by other artists. Notice the various objects they use.

2. Choose some objects for a picture and arrange them so that you can often look at them while drawing or painting your own picture. If available, laminate or use contact paper to cover your picture so that it can be used for a placemat.

3. Tell your friends and family about your placemat. You might tell them why you chose the objects for your placemat and what you liked best about making your picture.

Name: _____

THINKING ABOUT RACHEL RUYSCH AND ME

Respond to four or more of the following questions/statements:

1. Write the name of the city and the country where Rachel Ruysch was born..

2. What do you find most interesting about Rachel Ruysch's work as a still life painter?

3. List the names of at least three artists who painted still life pictures. Also list the objects they used in each of the pictures.

4. If you create another still life picture, what objects do you think you will use in it? Why?

5. Since you have studied and created a still life picture, do you think that you will appreciate still-life pictures more than you did before you studied them? Why?

6. Write one or more paragraphs about what you have learned about this artist and/or what you have learned through your own creative project relating to this artist. Write this information on the opposite side of this sheet or on a separate sheet of paper.

Toulouse-Lautrec
(too LOOZ low TREK)
1864–1901

Unlike many of his contemporaries, Henri de Toulouse-Lautrec did not worry about the sale of his paintings. Since his parents were wealthy French aristocrats, Toulouse-Lautrec did not concern himself with money or success. Nevertheless Toulouse-Lautrec became one of the most famous artists to emerge from the Impressionist movement in the nineteenth century. Known for his heavily lined drawings and pure color (which show the influence of the Japanese print artists Hokusai and Hiroshige), Toulouse-Lautrec is also famous for his many drawings of the nightlife in Montmartre, the entertainment district of Paris. Here, Toulouse-Lautrec became the first painter to unite his art with advertising by creating many posters for the theatrical shows playing in Montmartre. Toulouse-Lautrec made Montmartre his home and was very fond of the entertainers, dancers, artists, and circus performers who inhabited the theaters, dance halls, restaurants, and night clubs in the area.

Henri de Toulouse-Lautrec was born in Albi, a town in southern France, on November 24, 1864. Henri liked to draw as a child, he did not vigorously pursue his artistic inclinations until adolescence. It was only when he was fourteen years old, and he had broken both his legs in two separate accidents and was confined to bed, that he pursued drawing. As a result of the accidents, Henri's legs never properly healed. His legs stopped growing and Henri's full height as an adult was less than five feet.

Henri's childhood art teacher was a man by the name of Princeteau. It was Princeteau and Henri's father who first took him to the circus to see the horses perform. Henri's father, Alphonse, was fascinated with horses and passed on his admiration to Henri who grew to have a great interest and skill for painting horses in action. In the painting *Count de Toulouse-Lautrec Driving the Mail Coach to Nice* (1881), which hangs in the Musée du Petit Palais in Paris, Henri has painted his father driving a team of four galloping horses. In another painting entitled *In the Circus Fernando: The Ringmaster* (1888), hanging in The Art Institute of Chicago, Henri has painted a determined ringmaster, his whip in hand, supervising a galloping horse and its rider as they circle swiftly around the circus arena.

When Henri decided to pursue painting full-time, his mother provided him with her apartment in Paris. While Henri was in Paris he met many other artists, one of whom was the Dutch Impressionist painter, Vincent van Gogh. Toulouse-Lautrec and Van Gogh exhibited their works at the Goupil Gallery where van Gogh's brother, Theo, worked. While in Paris, Henri painted a portrait of his friend Vincent in pastel chalks. Later Henri suggested to Vincent that he travel to the countryside and paint. Vincent van Gogh took Henri's advice and painted many of his most beautiful and famous paintings in Arles, a town south of Paris in the French countryside. Toulouse-Lautrec also painted a portrait of another fellow artist, the Polish sculptor Cipa Godebsky. In the portrait we see a strong-looking bearded man, smoking a pipe with a humorous expression on his face.

But perhaps the most famous portraits Toulouse-Lautrec painted were those of the dancers and entertainers he befriended in the Parisian district of Montmartre. Toulouse-Lautrec had a studio in Montmartre and enjoyed observing and participating in the festive nightlife of the theaters and cafés there. Toulouse-Lautrec soon began to prefer drawing over paint because drawing allowed him to quickly execute lively lines capturing precise movements. His drawings of many entertainers — Jane Avril, May Belfort, La Goulouse, and Yvette Guilbert, captured their characteristic gestures, whether they were dancing or simply walking home from work.

Perhaps Toulouse-Lautrec's greatest contribution to the art world was his use of lithography, a form of printing. Toulouse-Lautrec drew with colored crayons on limestone which was then printed on paper. Using this technique he was able to produce posters for one of his favorite night clubs, the Moulin Rouge. *Jane Avril at the Jardin de Paris* (1893) is one of Toulouse-Lautrec's famous lithographs capturing the dancer performing on stage.

Henri de Toulouse-Lautrec died when he was only thirty-seven years old, the same age at which his friend Vincent van Gogh died. In the painting *At the Moulin Rouge* (1892), hanging in The Art Institute of Chicago, Toulouse-Lautrec depicts not only the gay night life he enjoyed, but we see him as well, in the center of the painting, a short, dark, bearded man passing through the night club with his cousin and friend, Gabriel de Celeyran.

Many of Toulouse-Lautrec's works are displayed in a museum dedicated to him in his hometown of Albi.

Name: _____

HENRI DE TOULOUSE-LAUTREC

VOCABULARY: motion, realistic, signature, demonstration

MATERIALS: tagboard or poster paper, paints and/or crayons

ACTIVITIES:

1. Read about and observe some of the posters that Toulouse-Lautrec created. Then design a poster about something that you like to do. You might, for example, make a poster relating to your hobby, a magic show, or a musical program. Will your poster convey motion? Will the people and objects look realistic? Be sure to put your signature on your poster.

2. Prepare a demonstration or presentation that relates to your poster. At a designated time, present these materials to the class.

Evaluation Sheet   Name: _____

HENRI DE TOULOUSE-LAUTREC

Respond to four or more of the following questions/statements:

1. Write the name of the famous nightclub that inspired many of Toulouse-Lautrec's drawings.

2. List two titles of Toulouse-Lautrec's works and the names of the museums where they can be found.

3. What was Henri de Toulouse-Lautrec's handicap? What do you think he did to overcome his handicap?

4. Observe a photograph of a painting by Toulouse-Lautrec. Then write three interesting facts that you discovered through your observation.

5. Write a description of one of Henri de Toulouse-Lautrec's paintings that you have studied. At a designated time read the description aloud and ask others to guess the title of the paintings that you described.

6. Write one or more paragraphs about what you have learned about this artist and/or what you have learned through your own creative project relating to this artist. Write this information on the opposite side of this sheet or on a separate sheet of paper.

　　　　　　　　　Name: _____

AN ARTIST'S PALETTE

MATERIALS:　　　colored construction paper for base of the palette, white paper for the splotches of paint, scissors, watercolors, brushes

DIRECTIONS FOR PAPER PALETTE:

1. Draw and cut out an artist's palette (base only) from colored construction paper.

2. Choose an artist and write a clue about the artist on each of the paint splotches. Cover each splotch with a different shade of thin watercolor paint. Draw a picture on the palette that relates to the artist.

ACTIVITIES:

1. Read a book about a specific artist. Then design your palette to portray various information about his/her life as an artist. Show your palette to others and explain what you are conveying about the artist.

2. After reading about the artists in this book, design a palette to portray the life of one of them. After you have completed your palette, show it to others and ask them to guess the name of the artist that is represented on the palette.

MUSEUM/GALLERY VISIT REPORT FORM

Your Name: _____ Teacher: _____

NAME & LOCATION OF MUSEUM/GALLERY: _____

_____

DATE OF VISIT: _____

ARTIST'S NAME: _____

DATE OF WORK: _____

TITLE: (if there is one) _____

MATERIALS: (medium) _____

Describe what you see:

Does this piece affect your feelings/senses in any way? Describe:

If you had to grade or rate this piece of artwork on a scale of 1 to 10, what score would you give it and why? Circle the score: 1   2   3   4   5   6   7   8   9   10

BIOGRAPHY/AUTOBIOGRAPHY
(of an artist outside of this book)

Your Name:_____ Teacher: _____

ARTIST: _____

TITLE OF BOOK: _____

PUBLISHER: _____

WHERE DOES (OR DID) THIS ARTIST LIVE? _____

MATERIALS: (medium) _____

_____

WHAT MEDIUM OR MEDIA DOES (OR DID) THIS ARTIST USE?

_____

Write at least three interesting things you have learned about the artist from your readings:

Explain why this person became famous:

Name three or more titles or descriptions of works by this artist:

CREATIVE ART PROJECT
(for independent learning)

Your Name:_____   Teacher: _____

MATERIALS NEEDED:_____

PLANS FOR CREATIVE PROJECT: _____

_____

_____

_____

ADULT APPROVAL: _____

Did you have any problems in creating your project? Why or why not?

What did you learn from creating this project that will help you to do better on your next art project?

Make a sketch of your finished project and write a brief description of it.

READ TO DISCOVER INFORMATION ABOUT A DIFFERENT ARTIST

Artist: _____   Name: _____

MEDIA MATERIALS
Find and read from at least three sources about the artist:

Title of Resource	Where was it obtained

INFORMATION DISCOVERED ABOUT THE ARTIST

_____

_____

_____

_____

_____

_____

_____

_____

_____

_____

GLOSSARY

abstract art–artistic works based on real people, places and things but which does not look like the real people, places and things; this style emphasizes colors, lines and geometrical forms.

anatomy–the study of the structure and parts of the human body, plants, or animals.

apprentice–a person who works with a more experienced person to learn a trade.

background–the area that is, or appears to be, in the back, (e.g., behind the main object in a picture).

botany–the science of studying plants and the way they grow.

challenges–often difficult tests of a person's abilities.

Classical Period– artwork which models the style used in ancient Greece and Rome.

collection–a group of things.

compare–to identify how things are alike.

composition–the organization of the parts of a work (e.g. the organization of the parts of the painting.)

contrast–to identify how things are different.

convey–to explain, (e.g., to explain an idea).

create–to cause to come into being; to make happen.

Cubism–a style of painting and sculpture developed in the early 20th century that uses formal geometric shapes.

demonstration–showing how something is used or how it works.

detail–a specific, or particular part of something.

dominant–controlling; ruling.

effect–result, consequence.

environment–the surrounding things or conditions in a setting.

facial expression–a look on a person's face which shows how the person feels, e.g. a smile or a frown.

fascinate–to capture the interest.

foreground–the part of the picture that is, or appears to be, in the front, (e.g., in front of the main object in the picture).

fresco–the technique of painting in water colors on wet plaster.

frontier–the part of a country which is at the edge or just beyond an unsettled area or a wilderness.

geometric–of geometry, (e.g. shapes such as triangles and rectangles).

history–the study of past events.

illustrator–a person who draws a picture representing a story or topic.

image–a likeness, a replica, or a copy.

Impressionism–an art movement that emphasized color, light, and emotion rather than detail.

industrial photographer–a photographer of business or industrial areas.

industry–manufacturing and business.

invention–an original creation.

labor–work; a group of workers.

landscape–a painting using outdoor scenery as the subject.

marble–a type of limestone that is used to make sculptures.

masterpiece–an artwork that was completed with a skill that is of superior quality.

middle ground–the part of the picture that is, or appears to be, in the middle, (e.g., between the foreground and background of a picture).

motion–movement.

mural–a large painting or drawing usually done on a wall.

object–a thing which can be touched and seen.

observe–to watch; to notice; to see.

ordinary–something that is usual or regular.

painting styles–different ways of painting that are set apart from others because of a particular form, appearance or characteristic.

perspective–how something looks from a certain position; (e.g., in a painting a close object looks big and a far object looks small).

plexiglas–a lightweight, durable type of plastic.

porcelain–a strong ceramic material through which light can pass.

portrait–a painting, drawing, or photograph that represents a person.

poster–a sign picture designed to be posted, shown in public.

professional photographer–one who earns money from his/her photographs.

proportion–the size of a thing in relation to other things.

realistic–real or practical.

relief sculpture–a piece of sculpture worked on a flat surface so that it stands out somewhat from the flat surface.

Renaissance–the period of history of the rebirth of art, literature and learning in Europe during the 14th, 15th, 16th, and 17th centuries.

representation–the artist's version of what an object looks like.

reveal–to show; to make known.

sculptor–a person who creates a three dimensional piece of art from design through construction.

sculpture–art in a three dimensional form.

self-expression–how one expresses or asserts oneself to others.

shade–a color with black added.

shadow–the darkness or the dark shape cast on a surface by an object cutting off the light.

shallow–not deep.

signature–a person's own handwritten name.

simulate–to imitate; to pretend; (e.g., to smile when you are sad).

situation–something that is occurring or has occurred at a particular place and time.

sketch–a simple drawing without details.

space–an area.

still life–subject matter which includes unmoving objects such as apples or chairs which are painted or drawn.

style–the method or manner of doing something.

surface–the outer face of an object.

symbol–a sign, mark or object that stands for another object or idea.

synthetism–a style of art using simplified form, bold color, extreme shapes and decorative effects.

technique–the way something is done.

texture–the surface feeling or look of an object or thing.

three-dimensional–having or seeming to have the dimension of depth as well as width and height.

value–degree of lightness and darkness in colors.

war correspondent–a person who is hired by the news media to write stories and articles about a war, usually from the war zone.

World War II–a war fought between 1939 and 1945. France, Great Britain, the Soviet Union, the United States and others fought against Japan, Germany, and Italy.

ARTIST BIBLIOGRAPHY

BONHEUR, ROSA

Epstein, Vivian Sheldon
History of Women Artists for Children. Denver, Colorado: VSE Publisher, 1989, pp. 13.
Price, Olive
Rosa Bonheur: Painter of Animals. Champaign, Illinois: Garrard Publishing Company, 1972.
Richardson, Wendy and Jack
Animals: Through the Eyes of Artists. (The World of Art). Chicago: Childrens Press, 1991, pp. 22–23.
Turner, Robyn Montana
Rosa Bonheur (Portraits of Women Artists of Children). Boston: Little, Brown and Co., 1991.

BOURKE-WHITE, MARGARET

Drafron, Carolyn
Margaret Bourke-White (American Women of Achievement). New York: Chelsea House Publishers, 1988.
Goldberg, Vicki
Margaret Bourke-White: A Biography. New York: Harper & Row, 1986.
Iverson, Genie
Margaret Bourke-White: News Photographer. Mankato, Minnesota: Creative Education, 1980.
Siegel, Beatrice
An Eye on the World: Margaret Bourke-White, Photographer. New York: Frederick Warne, 1980.
Silverman, Jonathon
For the World to See: The Life of Margaret Bourke-White. New York: Viking Press, 1983.
Sufrin, Mark
Focus on America: Profiles of Nine Photographers. New York: Charles Scribner's Sons, 1987, pp. 116–134.

DA VINCI, LEONARDO

Harris, Nathaniel
Leonardo & the Renaissance. New York: Macmillan Children's Group, 1987.
Lafferty, Peter
Leonardo da Vinci. New York: Watts, 1990.
Marshall, Norman V.
Leonardo da Vinci. Illus. by Aldo Ripamonti. Englewood Cliffs, New Jersey: Silver Burdett Press, 1990.
Raboff, Ernest
Leonardo da Vinci. (Art for Children). New York: Harper and Row, 1987.
Ventura, Piero
Great Painters. New York: G.P. Putnam's Sons, 1984, pp. 46–49 and 149.

GAUGUIN, PAUL

Raboff, Ernest
Paul Gauguin. (Art for Children). New York: Harper and Row, 1988.
Richardson, Wendy and Jack
Families: Through the Eyes of Artists. (The World of Art). Chicago: Childrens Press, 1991, pp. 8–9.
Richardson, Wendy and Jack
Natural World: Through the Eyes of Artists. (The World of Art). Chicago: Childrens Press, 1991, pp. 28–29.
Roalf, Peggy
Looking At Paintings: Cats. New York: Hyperion Books, 1992, pp. 28–29.
Ventura, Piero
Great Painters. New York: G.P. Putnam's Sons, 1984, pp. 133 and 147.

GOYA, FRANCISCO

Blizzard, Gladys S.
Come Look With Me: Enjoying Art With Children. Charlottesville, Virginia: Thomasson-Grant, 1990, pp. 10–11.
Venezia, Mike
Getting to Know the World's Greatest Artists: Francisco Goya. Chicago: Childrens Press, 1991.
Ventura, Piero
Great Painters. New York: G.P. Putnam's Sons, 1984, pp. 114–115.

HOKUSAI, KATSUSHIKA

Richard, Wendy and Jack
Water: Through the Eyes of Artists. (The World of Art). Chicago: Childrens Press, 1991, pp. 16–17.
The World Book Encyclopedia
The World Book Encyclopedia, Vol. 9. Chicago: World Book, Inc., 1992. pp. 289–290.

HOPPER, EDWARD

Blizzard, Gladys S.
Come Look With Me: Exploring Landscape Art with Children. Charlottesville, Virginia: Thomasson-Grant, 1992, pp. 24–25.
Roalf, Peggy
Looking At Paintings: Seascapes. New York: Hyperion Books, 1992, pp. 36–37.
Venezia, Mike
Edward Hopper: Getting to Know the World's Greatest Artists. Chicago: Childrens Press, 1990.

KLEE, PAUL

Raboff, Ernest
  Paul Klee. (Art For Children). New York: Harper & Row, Publishers.
Richardson, Wendy and Jack
  Entertainers: Through the Eyes of Artists. (The World of Art). Chicago: Childrens Press, 1991, pp. 38–39.
Richardson, Wendy and Jack
  The World of Art Entertainers. Chicago: Childrens Press, 1991, pp. 38–39.
Roalf, Peggy
  Looking At Paintings: Cats. New York: Hyperion Books, 1992, pp. 36–37.
Venezia, Mike
  Paul Klee: Getting to Know the World's Greatest Artists. Chicago: Childrens Press, 1991.

MICHELANGELO

Raboff, Ernest
  Michelangelo: Art For Children. New York: Harper & Row, Publishers, 1988.
Venezia, Mike
  Michelangelo: Getting to Know the World's Greatest Artists. Chicago: Childrens Press, 1991.
Ventura, Piero
  Great Painters. New York: G.P. Putnam's Sons, 1984, pp. 70–74 and 151.
Woolf, Felicity
  Picture This: A First Introduction to Paintings. New York: Doubleday, 1989, p. 12, 13, 36.

NEVELSON, LOUISE

Bober, S. Natalie
  Breaking Tradition: The Story of Louise Nevelson. New York: Atheneum, 1984.
Epstein, Vivian Sheldon
  History of Women Artists for Children. Denver, Colorado: VSE Publisher, 1989. p. 19.
Cain, Michael
  Louise Nevelson. New York: Chelsea House, 1989.

PICASSO, PABLO

Blizzard, Gladys S.
  Come Look With Me: Enjoying Art with Children. Charlottesville, Virginia: Thomasson-Grant, 1990, pp. 28–31.
Giraudy, Daniele
  Pablo Picasso: The Minotaur, An Art Play Book. New York: Abrams, Harry N., Inc., 1988.
Lyttle, Richard B.
  Pablo Picasso: The Man & the Image. New York: Macmillan Children's Group, 1989.
Raboff, Ernest
  Pablo Picasso: Art For Children. New York: Harper & Row, Publishers, 1982.
Richardson, Wendy and Jack
  Entertainers: Through the Eyes of Artists. (The World of Art). Chicago: Childrens Press, 1991, pp. 12–13.

Roalf, Peggy
    Seascapes: Looking At Paintings. New York: Hyperion Books, 1992, pp. 42–43.
Rodari, Florian
    A Weekend With Picasso. New York: Rizzoli, 1991.
Sommer, Robin L. and Patricia MacDonald
    Pablo Picasso, New York: Silver Burdette Press, 1990.
Venezia, Mike
    Picasso: Getting to Know the World's Greatest Artists. Chicago: Childrens Press, 1988.
Ventura, Piero
    Great Painters. New York: G.P. Putnam's Sons, 1984, pp. 140–141 and 151.
Woolf, Felicity
    Picture This: A First Introduction to Paintings. New York: Doubleday, 1989, p. 29, 36.

RAPHAEL

Raboff, Ernest
    Raphael. (Art For Children). New York: Harper & Row, Publishers, 1988.
Richardson, Wendy and Jack
    Families: Through the Eyes of Artist. (The World of Art). Chicago: Childrens Press, 1991, pp. 12–13.
Ventura, Piero
    Great Painters. New York: Putnam's Sons, 1984, pp. 58–60.
Woolf, Felicity
    Picture This: A First Introduction to Paintings. New York: Doubleday, 1989, p. 25.

REMINGTON, FREDERIC

Mc Cracken, Harold
    The Frederic Remington Book: A Pictorial History of the West. New York: Doubleday, 1966.
Raboff, Ernest
    Frederic Remington. (Art For Children). New York: Harper & Row, Publishers, 1988.
Remington, Frederic
    Frederic Remington's Own West. New York: Dial, 1960.

RENOIR, PIERRE-AUGUSTE

Blizzard, Gladys S.
    Come Look With Me: Enjoying Art with Children. Charlottsville, Virginia: Thomasson-Grant, 1990, pp. 26–27.
Raboff, Ernest
    Pierre-Auguste Renoir. (Art For Children). New York: Harper & Row, Publishers, 1987.
Richardson, Wendy and Jack
    Cities: Through the Eyes of an Artist. (The World of Art). Chicago Childrens Press, 1991, pp. 26–27.
Roalf, Peggy
    Looking At Paintings: Cats. New York: Hyperion Books, 1992, pp. 22–23.
Roalf, Peggy
    Looking At Paintings: Dancers. New York: Hyperion Books, 1992, pp. 36–37.

Skira-Venturi, Rosabianca
  A Weekend With Renoir. New York: Rizzoli, 1990.
Thomas, David
  Renoir. London: The Medici Society, Ltd., 1980.
Ventura, Piero
  Great painters. New York: G.P. Putnam's Sons, 1984, pp. 136–137, 152, 153.
Woolf, Felicity
  Picture This: A First Introduction to Paintings. New York: Doubleday, 1989, p. 26, 27.

RIVERA, DIEGO

Cockcroft, James
  Diego Rivera. New York: Chelsea House, 1991.
Gleiter, Jan and Kathleen Thompson
  Diego Rivera. (Raintree Hispanic Stories). Illus. by Yoshi Miyake. Milwaukee, Wisconsin: Raintree, 1989.
Hargrove, Jim
  Diego Rivera: Mexican Muralist. Chicago: Childrens Press, 1990.
Richardson, Wendy and Jack
  Cities: Through the Eyes of an Artist. (The World of Art). Chicago: Childrens Press, 1991, pp. 46–47.
Winter, Jeanette - Text by Jonah Winter
  Diego. New York: Alfred Knopf, 1991.

ROCKWELL, NORMAN

Finch, Christopher
  Norman Rockwell 332 Magazine Covers Book. New York: Abbeville Press, 1979.
Finch, Christopher
  50 Norman Rockwell Favorites. New York: Crown Publishers, 1977.

ROUSSEAU, HENRI

Blizzard, Gladys S.
  Come Look With Me: Exploring Landscape Art with Children. Charlottesville, Virginia: Thomasson-Grant, 1992, pp. 16–17.
Raboff, Ernest
  Henri Rousseau: Art For Children. New York: Harper & Row, Publishers, 1989.
Richardson, Wendy and Jack
  Families: Through the Eyes of Artists. (The World of Art). Chicago: Childrens Press, 1991, pp. 36–37.

RUYSCH, RACHEL

Epstein, Vivian Sheldon
  History of Women Artists for Children. Denver, Colorado: VSE Publisher, 1989, pp. 8–9.
Woolf, Felicity
  Picture This: A First Introduction to Paintings. New York: Doubleday, 1989, pp. 7, 9, 36.

TOULOUSE-LAUTREC, HENRI DE

Roalf, Peggy
Looking At Paintings: Dancers. New York: Hyperion Books, 1992, pp. 32-33.
Raboff, Ernest
Henrie de Toulouse-Lautrec. New York: Harper and Row, 1988.
Richardson, Wendy and Jack
Animals Through the eyes of Artists. (The World of Art). Chicago: Childrens Press, 1991, pp. 24–25.
Richardson, Wendy and Jack
Entertainers: Through the Eyes of Artists. (The World of Art.) Chicago: Childrens Press, 1991, pp. 30–31
Ventura, Piero
Great Painters. New York: Putnam's Sons, 1984, pp. 132, 134–135, 154.

BOOKS FOR PARENTS AND TEACHERS

Brooks, Susan W. and Susan M. Senatori
   SEE THE PAINTINGS! A Handbook for Art Appreciation in the Classroom. Rosemont, New Jersey: Modern Learning Press, 1988.

Burrough, Lea
   Introducing Children To The Arts: A Practical Guide for Librarians and Educators. Boston: G.K. Hall & Co., 1988.

Edwards, Betty
   Drawing on the Artist Within. New York: Simon and Schuster, 1986.

Edwards, Betty
   Drawing on the Right Side of the Brain. Los Angeles, California: J.P. Tarcher, 1979.

Heller, Nancy G.
   Women Artists: An Illustrated History. New York: Abbeville Press, 1987.

Murray, Peter and Linda
   Dictionary of Art and Artists. New York: Penguin Books, 1989.

Museum Guide Publications
   1992 Traveler's Guide to Art Museum Exhibitions. New York: Harry N. Abrams, 1992.

Rosen, Randy and Catherine C. Brawer
   Making Their Mark: Women Artists Move into the Mainstream, 1970–85. New York: Abbeville Press, 1989.

Warner, Sally
   Encouraging the Artist in Your Child: Even if You Can't Draw. New York: St. Martin's Press, 1989.

Wilson, Marjorie and Brent
   Teaching Children to Draw: A Guide for Teachers and Parents. Englewood Cliffs, New Jersey: Prentice-Hall, 1982.

PARENT/TEACHER NOTES

PARENT/TEACHER NOTES